THE
REGULARS'
TABLE

THE REGULARS' TABLE

Christina R. Griffin

International Psychoanalytic Books (IPBooks)
New York • http://www.IPBooks.net

Published by International Psychoanalytic Books (IPBooks)
Queens, New York
Online at: www.IPBooks.net

Disclaimer

Every effort has been made to ensure that this book is free from error or omissions. Information provided is of general nature only and should not be considered legal or financial advice. The intent is to offer a variety of information to the reader. However, the author, publisher, editor or their agents or representatives shall not accept responsibility for any loss or inconvenience caused to a person or organisation relying on this information.

Book cover design and formatting services by BookCoverCafe.com

www.IPBooks.net

ISBN: 978-1-949093-05-6 (pbk)

Table of Contents

I dedicate this book to David,
who has steadfastly supported my imagination and
shared the value of creativity and invention in our life together.

Chapter 1

Desire

Ten years ago, I was a psychoanalyst in a beautiful coastal community. Often, I was struck by an awareness of the abyss between the beauty of my surroundings and the gulag of my interior world. How I became aware of these feelings, why they were such important signals, and what they ultimately revealed to me provided the genesis for this book. There were a multitude of personal questions as to why I had these feelings. What was my cultural context as I practiced and lived? My subjective experience as a psychoanalyst in this gulag? The Siberia-like experience did not have much in common with life by the sea. But then, one part of psychoanalysis is about what is beneath that surface.

Frequently, I had conversations with clients about their own gulags. Some clients felt constricted by choice or fate. Some had lost connection with others or with themselves. Some described feeling that their passion could not be realized. All of them needed hope. The spirit does not do well in confinement. I could relate.

Back then, I noticed my dissociated, preoccupied mind would depart for a distant place. Whether it was due to an intellectual or emotional loneliness, the feeling of being in a gulag was

contemporary in nature. Familiar with spells of ennui and restlessness, I thought that this phenomenon had to do with my
circumstances, but because of its persistence and grip on me, I
gradually realized that my experience was atavistic. This discovery
raised questions I was unable to answer at the time and could only
address by reflecting about my dreams. My dreams held preserved
memories, curiously offering me emotional continuity from other
lives in other centuries.

Social cues would catch my attention that seemed innocuous
to others, such as a friend's feigned yawn when psychoanalysis
was mentioned, or a spark ignited in another's eye that indicated
interest, a turning towards rather than away. A passionate person, I was impatient, sometimes discouraged, but uninterested
in changing others or selling what was interesting to me. I did
not want to teach or proselytize, only to wander, explore and,
flâneuse-like, observe. I developed several behaviors: I was a quick
study in superficial conversation which helped me navigate away
from what I didn't want toward something better, and I had a
willful disregard of anything irrelevant. I needed more—a kind of
mutual recognition. I desired emotional imagination as well as
analytic intellect, and even more, an abundance of felt life, the
irresistible aliveness that is palpable in another's mind. This was
the dream of a romantic.

By writing, studying, and paying attention to conversations
that evoked particular emotions, I developed a space where I
could take risks, contained within an emotional sphere. I wanted
to live with more depth and meaning between friends and me and
explore the reasons this was not happening for me; I sought to un-
cover aspects of myself that were responsible, understand them,

and explore fully my private world of desire. I sensed that it was the presence of a trusted other that would create the mutuality. I longed for the kind of bodily sense of another, without words, familiarly and unconditionally. It was that kind of recognition from another person, deeper than consciousness, which connected me to passion.

Desire, that mysterious combination of longing and love, had always been important to me. I know now what I didn't know then, that my desire would take me back in time and transform my present life. What was so surprising about the adventure I began was the form it took. While reading historic Hungarian correspondence, personal essays, and eulogies, I discovered an emotional tone of love in the authors' deep, enduring relationships. I did not know much about Hungary. I had no conscious connection to the country, yet I felt an emotional affinity for the place, its history, and the culture. This was the shape of my desire. I was drawn to this place and its people.

In 2012, I read a eulogy for Hungarian psychoanalyst Sándor Ferenczi, written by his closest friend, Hugó Veigelsberg, known as "Ignotus." It was published on May 28, 1933 in the Budapest daily newspaper, *Magyar Hirlap*, a few days after Ferenczi's funeral. For years, the two men met every Sunday afternoon in Ferenczi's office. They sat in silence, passing scraps of paper to each other—an experiment in thought transference. The emotion Veigelsberg's words transmitted, their spirit, rose up from the page and penetrated my heart. Most of the details and evidence were lost to time, but the suggestion of private, experimental, intimate writings was kindling for my imagination. I was powerfully affected by the passion in their friendship. I knew I would do everything to replicate their experiment, to make this happen for myself. I had no choice. Thus, I began to investigate Ferenczi's life and those of his friends.

Sándor Ferenczi (7 July, 1873–22 May, 1933) was a Hungarian psychoanalyst and key theorist of psychoanalysis. He was a close associate of Sigmund Freud, president of the International Psychoanalytic Association from 1918-1919, and founder of the Budapest School of Psychoanalysis. In 1919, he was the world's first university professor of psychoanalysis. He was known for working with the most difficult patients and developing a theory of more active intervention, as well as for the introduction of clinical empathy, the "confusion of tongues" theory of trauma, his openness to the traumatic histories of his patients, and his book, *Thalassa: A Theory of Genitality* (1924). He had a strong influence on the early development of the interpersonal theory of personality in the United States. The publication of *The Clinical Diary of Sándor Ferenczi* in 1985 and the first volume of *The Correspondence of Sigmund Freud and Sándor Ferenczi* in 1992 created a renaissance of interest in Ferenczi's work. In the next decade, two more volumes of their correspondence were published. The International Sándor Ferenczi Conferences have been held regularly since 1991.

Ferenczi's friend, Veigelsberg (1869-1949), was a writer, poet, critic, editor, and organizer. In addition to Ignotus (Latin for *unknown*), he wrote under the pseudonyms Dixi, Pato, Pal, Mrs. Emma (13 years of the *Mrs. Emma Letters*) and Tar Lorincz. He was one of the first adherents and supporters of Freudian psychoanalysis in Hungary. In 1913, when the Hungarian Psychoanalytic Association was founded, he was the only literary member (the others were physicians). He was distinguished for the lyric individuality of his poems, stories, and sociological works. Along with Miksa Fenyő and Reno Usuat, Veigelsberg was a founder of the literary magazine *Nyugat* in 1908 and was considered the most influential literary critic of his time. He was a proponent of the autonomy of literature, of *l'art pour l'art*—art for art's sake, or art independent of politics. He was one of Ferenczi's oldest and closest friends.

Michael Balint (1896-1970), a Hungarian psychoanalyst, began attending Ferenczi lectures after completing his medical studies in Budapest. At age 21, he became interested in psychoanalysis and met the psychoanalyst Imre Hermann. He and his wife Alice Kovács began a training analysis with Ferenczi. Balint became Ferenczi's disciple and literary executor. He also studied with István Hollós and Géza Róheim. In the 1920s, he assumed a leading role in Hungarian psychoanalysis. When Ferenczi died in 1933, Balint became administrator of his estate and his successor as director of the Budapest Polyclinic. Balint spent the latter half of his life in England and was a proponent of object relations theory.

Frigyes Karinthy (1887-1938) was a writer, poet, playwright, journalist, satirist, and translator who was analyzed by Ferenczi. Karinthy argued that "art cannot exist without science." He was a friend of Dezső Kosztolányi and Géza Csáth, who later introduced him to Freud. Beginning in 1912, his book, *You Write Like This?*, a literary parody, dynamically into popular literature, followed by *It Is Snowing, The Ballad of Dumb Men, Fools Encyclopedia,* and *Curved Mirror*. He was the first to criticize feared dictators Benito Mussolini, Adolf Hitler, and Josef Stalin. In 1937, he published *Journey Around my Skull*, which detailed his brain surgery. Known for a dry sense of humor, he noted in a well-known comment: "In humor I know no jokes." His story, *Chains*, included his concept of six degrees of separation.

Kosztolányi (1885-1936) was a poet, novelist, and critic who was also analyzed by his friend Ferenczi, whose alter ego, Dr. Movister, appears in one of Kosztolányi's most famous novels. Kosztolányi's first volume of poetry was published in 1907, when he then joined the *Nyugat* circle led by Ignotus. In 1910, he achieved immediate success with a volume of poems, *The Complaints of a Poor Child*. Kosztolányi was a sympathetic observer of human frailty, and his numerous short stories showed a gentle humor and a penchant for the macabre. He, too, was dedicated to the principle of art for art's sake. His novels, *Anna Édes* (1926) and *Wonder Maid* (1947), show his concern with artistic form. He took little interest in the social questions that absorbed most of the *Nyugat* circle.

Other friends and associates of Ferenczi included Sándor Márai (1900-1989) a journalist who also authored 46 books, mostly novels. He was one of the most influential representatives of middle class literature. His novels exhibit nostalgia for the bygone multiethnic, multicultural society of the Austro-Hungarian Empire. Notable novels include *The Rebels*, a family saga set at the end of the empire; *Casanova in Bolzano*, on romantic love; and *Portrait of a Marriage*, on the relationship between love and class and love and security; and *Embers*, on the bonds of male friendship. He is considered a genius in portraying humanity.

Within Ferenczi's circle was Endre Ady (1877-1919), whose *New Poems*, published in 1906, produced a literary explosion in Hungary. Once regarded a touchstone of modern Hungarian poetry, its impact bore testimony to the extraordinary importance of literature and poetry in Hungary at the time. Ady was a historical, political, and literary phenomenon. He was closely associated with the artistically progressive *Nyugat*, which he also edited in 1912. His fourth collection of poems, *Blood and Gold*, brought him success and critical acclaim. He was interested in politics and became a member of the radical group, Huszadik Szazad ("Twentieth Century"). In 1908, in Nagyvarad, he was one of the founders of a literary circle, A Holnap ("Tomorrow"). The circle published an anthology of poems by Ady and others, including Mihály Babits, Gyula Juhász, and Béla Balázs.

The coffeehouse was a Hungarian institution, a place where one could truly live. Ferenczi and his friends established a ritual of meeting regularly in chosen cafes. Ferenczi was at home with the literati. Kosztolányi recalled that Ferenczi "played" at society games: "He was interested in linguistics, in theatre, in puns, in gossip, in all that is human."[1] Ferenczi met with his friends "in the kavehaz (Turkish style coffeehouse), or at the table in the café at the Hotel Royal (where he lived as a bachelor, in spite of himself), or the wonderful Cafe New York."[2] These "popular universities" were full of writers, journalists, and students. According to literary critic György Lukács, "At a particular table—their reservation was sacrosanct—this or that group of journalists, playwrights, or sculptors and painters would congregate, usually presided over by one or two leading figures."[3] Often their preference was to work in the cafe, where at times entire newspaper articles, short stories, or chapters of a novel were composed.

> In those [cafes] frequented by journalists and writers, the headwaiters (some of whom were celebrated for their knowledge of literature) kept sheaves of long white sheets of paper (called 'dogs' tongues') available to any writer who

chose to compose his article or essay there.[4] Free pens and ink were also provided. One could hear Kosztolányi's unusual order: "Waiter, a bottle of... ink, please!"[5]

The members of this literary circle were all habitués of various Budapest coffee houses, especially the Café Royal, where Ferenczi held court. They all contributed to Ignotus's literary journal, *Nyugat*. Several of them and/or their spouses had been analysands of Ferenczi's and they all shared a fascination with the insights of psychoanalysis, as well as the gossip surrounding Freud and his circle.[6]

In these coffee houses, Ignotus and Ferenczi regularly met with other key writers, poets, editors, during the first and second generations of *Nyugat* writers. A group of avant-garde artists called *The Eight*, who gathered in the gardens of their member, painter Róbert Berény, also influenced the urban Budapest environment.

All of these groups had variegated relationships with one another which were complex, and these sometimes overlapping groups, along with the *Nyugat* writers, defined the intellectual environment of progressive Budapest. The coffeehouse culture played a prominent role in the Cultural Revolution. This culture was well connected with the press, perhaps more than anywhere else in Europe at the time.[7]

CHAPTER 2

Historia Docet

A s my research unfolded, the heart and mind of Ferenczi and his friends penetrated me. I entered a historic mindset and discovered aspects of myself. I wanted to live at the heart of what Ferenczi and his friends had created. Part of my process was independent and introspective; the other part, equally significant, took place among friends. Some gently led me, offering a welcomed hand. Others generously challenged me with their scholarship. All were comrades who met and engaged me. All of us possessed the serious intention of wanting more from each other and from life. Trusting my sense of *historia docet*, "history teaches," I traveled in my mind, in the minds of others, and to Hungary.

Cities in Hungary were strongly influenced by Protestant Calvinism. Debrecen, Budapest, and Miskolc, Ferenczi's birthplace, had prominent Calvinist schools. Ferenczi possessed an openness to friends of various religious faiths but, as a Jew, was expected to study Judaism. He lived close to the northeastern city Debrecen, the Calvinist Rome, and was educated at Miskolc Calvinist Gymnasium, finishing at age 17.

I, too, was strongly influenced by Calvinism as a Presbyterian minister's daughter. My associations to Calvinism were a mix of impressions: rigid and specific beliefs, the doctrine of predestination, the subversion of the Protestant Reformation, and a general sense that John Calvin was a misunderstood intellectual, his ideas being considered a form of reductionism. Still, my subjective experience was that Calvin had strict certainty, stern decisive judgment, and no ambiguity. There was no human warmth associated with his thoughts. I wondered whether there was a commonality between Jewish intellectuals who attended Calvinist schools and my own Calvinist influences, and whether we shared a formative exposure that may have opened the door to an attitude of tolerance and intellectual curiosity, both for me and for Ferenczi.

I was always silent about my experience of growing up in a Calvinist home and community. I gravitated toward others who seemed less restricted and in whom I sensed warmth and tolerance. There was an appeal and an *at home* feeling with the 'Budapest-type'—Ferenczi, his literati—and with certain Ferenczian scholars that I am fortunate to know. I related to the attitudes of these European intellectuals, past and present. A solidarity had emerged.

The Ferenczian capacity to "touch the unconscious" held me in its grip. It emboldened me to tolerate the risks involved, such as strange, intense relationships, particularly with men, who entered my life during the blossoming of *The Regulars' Table*. One man was Hungarian. I was told later, by another Hungarian, that this man "smelled me," referring to the Hungarian nose, that Ferenczian capacity to penetrate my unconscious. Another Hungarian man shared my Calvinist upbringing and also found refuge with intellectuals on the fringe. An American man came into my life as a fellow explorer, and we continue today to plumb the depths of emotion, attachments, love, and suffering in a silent, trusted space together, contained in the relief and frustration of a committed and complicated relationship.

I was following emotional footprints from the turn of the century and found myself among Ferenczi, "the mother of psychoanalysis," and the cabal of Hungarian writers, poets, artists, and physicians. From there I undertook a physical journey, departing the Central Coast of California to Baden-Baden, Toronto, Siracusa, and Budapest. The past informed the present as I became part of a migration of ideas.

Swept up in this current, I experienced the profound richness and expansive feelings of possibility that the new psychoanalytic view had brought to the Hungarian regulars long ago, and they transferred that expansiveness to my emotional gulag. The significant and enduring friendships between Ferenczi and Freud, Ignotus and Ferenczi, and Balint and Ferenczi have inspired my friendships. Their relationships were deep, enduring, and turbulent with emotion. I had analogous experiences in my relationships. My ongoing conversation, curiosity, and openness to these legendary minds created a powerful imaginary line between past and present. I traversed this line to channel the thoughts of Ferenczi and his associates. These intellectuals-with-a-heart have traveled far to a new world to tell their intimate story. Unconscious knowing and the transference of thoughts became an adventure which I could not resist. However, the regular's stories might be understood, they are, after all, in some form love stories.

We are all migrating outside of consciousness. It is the unconsciousness of desire, its surprise, the attractions and the resistances, that shape our lives. In the soul, past minds, passionate with intention, meet modern minds, recognizing kindred spirits.

I hoped that if I was lucky, I could sit down with my friends and continue the legacy at a new regulars' table.

Have I finally met some people with whom I can speak my mind? It has taken so long. It is such a satisfying experience to approach our gathering, to look forward to something rather than mourn the loss and observe what's missing—a conversation never satisfied, never found. Are they becoming friends who I can talk to unguardedly? Although I appreciate these friends and acquaintances for many reasons, I am aware of selecting and editing content to present here. Among this new group, I have another kind of conversation. Emergent and in the formative stages, this uninhibited conversation is exciting because it is a freedom. In secret, I hope the conversation will continue to thrive; although, at the edges of my mind, I am aware of the experience of time and that we, as a gathering, now have a past, present, and future. I am also aware that the experience of time is more palpable and alive, a reverie, transient and ephemeral. I am acutely reminded of transience because of these conversations which only occur at the regulars' table."[8]

I knew it when I felt it. *A coup de foudre*, bolt of lightning—two senses intertwined in a moment of recognition when there is a certain kind of collective energy of mind, as if experiencing fusion of thought and emotion. Passionate and new talking, moving forward and outward, expansive, emergent, unstoppable communing. Communion.

I knew it the moment I was in the surround. It had the feel of creating a new culture. The emotional landscape was inflected by the contours of desire. Then there was the location, the setting and preparation, arranging the table. The experience of approaching was important. My friends arrived from their journeys. They gathered, bringing their thoughts, evoked by associations of past experiences with each other. Then my favorite friends—the quiet and curious—came to sit. I knew them. I recognized and had come to trust them. We exchanged a few words and asked each other a question or two. Spontaneity and alertness developed and carried forth in the group, now infused with a particular energy. As Karinthy once said, "Those who have a lot to say are mostly modest."[9]

We focused our attention on what was being said and shared interest in the conversation. An energy emerged from our collective experience. I looked around the table and noticed that what I was looking for was occurring. I had intuited it would happen from the group's inception, the right combination of people again, and the timing. In the midst of what was happening, it was impossible not to notice and recognize the process in which I was immersed unless I consciously did something that would remove my mind just for a second—a dissociation from that very moment in order to realize what I had, what was occurring, and knowing that I had arrived—if only for a few minutes.

We were all there together at that point in time, gathered around our table. None of this moment could stay, remain permanent, and be possessed. *Please, couldn't we remain here a bit longer?* How could I retain the experience of time in my mind and be in the moment and also separate? I did not want this experience to vanish. Also in my awareness was my desire for them not to go away and never return. Kosztolányi wrote, "When people go away they vanish, turn to nothing, stop being. They live only in memories, haunting the imagination."[10]

At Ferenczi's regulars' table, in the uninhibited conversations, I can feel the heightened emotion. I imagine being there, spectator and participant. Saturated with the richness of freedom and desire, the table overflows. All my senses are pulled towards the scene. I possess in my mind a changing image, a photograph of the characters, principals and extras, in the dim café lighting. The melting effects of shading and light keep the walls of time permeable. The scene appears in shades of cream and sepia, like old photographs protected by canvas cloth, which must be lifted for viewing. The shifting images combine the power of memory and imagination against time. But it is the lighting that captures the scene as it creates romantic sensibilities and an attachment that involves all senses. The more senses engaged, the more vivid the memories will be. The café scenario, as these friends approached, left and returned again, involved an interplay of anticipation, retrospection, and restoration. It held the future, a hope for continuance. It comprised a ritual that accomplishes something for people when they are present and when they are absent. A communion—again that word with many strong associations.

There were many late nights at the Café Royal. Mutual affinity kept the regulars up into the wee hours. Psychoanalytic ideas about the unconscious mind and human experience were intertwined in Hungarian literature because of the personal relationships between Ferenczi and his many writer friends. These friends created the literary world in which they wanted to live. Ferenczi knew intuitively that these novelists and poets created imaginative truths that penetrated deeply into human experience. He saw that writing was the core of their enterprise. The regulars shared these conversations and came to see even more clearly, that many of the human questions posed by psychoanalysis could be traced in the literary-poetic prose of Hungarian writers, and they were in the center of it.

Upon Ferenczi's death in 1933, a number of notes were found among his papers. They were written in the four languages that served as the medium of his thought and intended only for private use. Balint, his literary executor and disciple, faced the great challenge of organizing and transcribing these notes. He was also faced with enormous personal grief from the loss of Ferenczi. He did not yet know what Ferenczi's work would come to mean to him and the way psychoanalysis would develop as a theory and a therapeutic process.

Ferenczi started with a blank page and scribbles on bits of paper. Notes and fragments turned into pages that existed for private use. I, too, started with a blank page, emulating him, and imagined him thinking: *These jottings of ideas need to be captured at the moment of thought. Personal shorthand, abbreviations, cryptic phrases, all difficult to decipher, that make sense only to me, as if in code. Later, if the occasion arises, these notes can be worked into a coherent form to share with others.*

CHAPTER 3

Michael Balint's Reverie, 1933

At the Ferenczi Villa in the hills of Buda, Balint reflects about Ferenczi...

As I climb these stairs to Sándor's office, I did not expect the sense of calm that is penetrating me while I trail my hand on the wrought iron banister, up the stairs to his office. Looking out the window to the shaded back yard, I feel the enormity of his contributions and an overwhelming sense of frustration and loss. Abruptly, I am flooded by waves of memory, impressions, and pieces of conversations. I am vexed with feelings of anger and sadness that are disturbing and immobilizing. I am also feeling the weight of my responsibility to the Hungarian Psychoanalytic Society to speak at your funeral.

Recently, I came here to be with you, and we enjoyed long periods of time together. Alone, without you now, I'm amazed at the discoveries I'm beginning to grasp. All of the documents scattered and placed here are part of you. I am grateful that I know your handwriting! I'm astounded as I begin piecing together your private musings, sparks of innovative, and still-experimental thinking from these scraps of papers. There must be thousands of documents in various forms. Many are just notes—random scribblings on scraps of papers, backs of envelopes, pharmaceutical propaganda pages. Then there is the typewritten copy of the complete correspondence between Freud and Ferenczi and his proper diary, typed

with numbered pages, more or less. A striking contrast. I knew about
these documents and those closest to you knew about the existence of
this diary. At least three of us, Vilma Kovács, Alice, and I, will read
the diary at first, as requested by Mrs. Ferenczi.[11]

I am surrounded by you. Your presence in this office, in my mind, in
the air, penetrating me with a force I haven't experienced before. I have
thought of nothing else since our visits these last few weeks when, though
your body was failing from pernicious anemia, your mind was clear,
challenging me and also challenging yourself, as was your way. Through
all the controversy your work with patients caused, I'm struck by how
even the most educated and sophisticated have had such a strong negative reaction to only a small part of information or even gossip about
something you did—declaring opinions without thorough investigation of
what they did not understand. You would eagerly explore the criticisms
when you were struck by something you didn't understand. What so
many do not know or care to realize about you was that your finely
nuanced mind combined with the force of your personality made possible
an honest critique of your own ideas and methods, even when you were
excited and proud of them as innovations and successful experiments.

I feel flooded by memories of you. I think of your experiment in
mutual analysis with Elizabeth Severn. You talked for months about
the analysis feeling stagnant. You pursued the idea of mutual analysis,
structuring sessions in a systematic way, double sessions or alternating
sessions, one for her and one for you, so that by using her interpreta-
tions, you might find your blind spots. I remember our discussions of this
impasse, the empathic failure. You were so interested in my perspective
and needed to talk. The product of our shared thoughts helped lead to a
new trauma-analysis, yes, mutual analysis, where you became mother
to your patient. Yes, I did support this individual experiment in mutual

analysis. You agreed to have your negative countertransference analyzed and invited your patient, Elizabeth, to help you. The change and progress in her analysis was so inspiring that you talked and wrote about this radical experiment. Then, you were vulnerable to being slaughtered by others' reactions. I sensed, and we discussed heatedly, your naiveté in exposing yourself to this difficult patient—the danger and risk in your method.

It seems to me now, sitting at your desk, that the upheaval you caused by exposing yourself to the wolves in such a vulnerable manner was inevitable. My faith remains in your work. On no account can you be accused of having agreed to mutual analysis out of a preference for the easy patient—she was not. You knew what a grave commitment this was and what a risk. I admire your ability to try an approach designed to illuminate blind spots as analyst, those shadowy corners—you intuited that it was important to locate each person, analyst and analysand, in relation to the other with greater assurance.[12]

You were often maligned, criticized for your creative and unorthodox ideas—misunderstood by the rigid academics, the political and unimaginative. Sándor, I wonder what it was like for you, living with such controversy stirred up by labels such as "the kissing technique," "advocating mutual analysis," "deep-seated needs for mother's love," "enfant terrible," and "the wild analyst"? I believe that what is not yet seen about you, for example, is how you gradually encountered a whole series of problems with mutual analysis. You did not rest on any sense of discovery but remained open to the questions themselves. Sándor, you are maligned by ignorance and possibly envy.

You were drawn to and experienced people with difficulties in your society, "the alcoholics, psychotic, sexopathic, others on the fringe"—you, the curious one, "penetrated their world beyond the conventional limits of traditional medicine through hypnosis, explorations of spiritualism, and alternative ways of thinking."[3] Unconventional, you challenged conventional thought.

I am amazed and moved by the radical way you expanded upon the boundaries of clinical empathy and activity as no analyst had done before or dared to consider. (I also find myself fearful; there is a corner of my heart that is traditional.) I know now, that I will write about this. I feel a weight, a responsibility for your work, and I fear your ideas will be lost, condemned, and wrongly judged. I was in a privileged position to understand the reasoning and yet be bold in my criticisms of your innovative and dangerous idea. I think today, how my place in this history was so much easier than yours, and I am glad that it was for you, not me, to dare.

The last few weeks with you were very painful. Bedridden, yet despite the effects of pernicious anemia, you were always ready to talk. On one of these visits, I thought about our long relationship from mentor to intimate friends. We were compassionate brothers, trusted confidants, seeking each other with ideas, challenging each other's skepticism. At times, we were insatiable.

It is painful when I think of your lifelong relationship with Freud, your struggle with different desires of and for each other: Freud, as the master, wanting a son who could follow and fulfill his vision, and you, Ferenczi, who, in time, wanted a strong personal relationship with mutual respect. Freud could not follow you along this particular road, yet both of you maintained a lifelong friendship, though fraught with differences both tolerable and unbearable.

Reading your notes and diary, I'm suffering with you now as I think of your last meeting with Freud. Your last diary entry, August 24, 1932, was before your trip to Vienna. I am making inferences on the basis of a *cursory reading of your notes, my knowledge of your medical condition, and my sense of your last visit in Vienna just prior to the Wiesbaden Congress. You suffered a shattering blow, again, from Freud. In Vienna, you read Freud your paper for the Congress: "Confusion of Tongues between Adults and the Child." Freud was deeply shocked by the contents of this paper and urged you not to publish until he had reconsidered the position put forth in it.[14] On several occasions, you discussed with me in detail your controversy with Freud and various plans to rewrite and expand on the ideas introduced in the paper. We met on the Sunday before your death, and even then, mentally, you were quite clear.[15]*

I am deeply troubled by your last encounter with Freud. You were profoundly shaken. Even in your final year diary entries, you were striving for mutuality with Freud and writing of your painful "rearranging and dying." I'm proud of you refusing to accommodate to Freud and, more recently, declining to be president of the International Psychoanalytic Association, which Freud wanted for you. I'm left with my own painful, unanswered questions as to how this conflict contributed to your death. You wrote only six pages after these October diary entries. This incident is powerfully reminiscent of another shattering between you and Freud—the Palermo, Sicily, trip in September, 1910. During a joint working session, which you had so eagerly anticipated, your independent attitude was much more than Freud was ever able to accept. During the remaining trip, you felt Freud's attitude was one of parental severity, authority, and reserve. You were reproached for behaving like a truculent and demanding child. This painful discord planted the seeds of a lifetime of struggle within your friendship with Freud, and I believe it undergirded and fueled the controversy and disparaging comments which followed you all of your life. Your openness to experimentation, innovation, and the unanswered mystery of the human mind were marginalized by many in the field. These judgments of your character strengthened the miscomprehension of and negative reactions to your ideas. Many could not, or would not, accept you, Ferenczi.[16, 17]

Words seem so important right now, but mine read like empty, discarded husks. I fail to capture the beauty of poetic words. For your interment, I want to be more like Márai, Ignotus, Kosztolányi, Krúdy, Jozef, Ady, but I don't possess their imagination. I recognize that I am passionate and capable, but I possess only an appreciation of it all. Sándor, many of us felt you were like a poet, though you didn't consider yourself such. You were also emotional and graceful in your writing when you wanted to be. I want to have unusually beautiful words for you and about you. We will all eventually write about you, but we must present ourselves in it. I must be myself. There is a possibility of beauty in my effort of telling your story. My love for you as a brother is also the love of beginnings. I will rest now to begin again tomorrow. Resurgam. I shall rise again.

Upon reflection, I see your ideas, writings, and basic stance towards people in moments that we experienced together. I remember discussing your theories on trauma and particularly on childhood sexual abuse. Words were so important but also understanding the silence. In the notes of these last few weeks, I find the language of tenderness, as you termed it in "The Confusion of Tongues between the Child and the Adult." This paper contains some of your most important ideas on understanding the unspoken language between child and adult. It has been formative in the way I think and work. You remarked once that words are unpredictable, often misinterpreted, and can contribute greatly to the confusion of tongues between one's patient and oneself. Vivid in my

memory is my early fascination with ideas about nonverbal aspects of the doctor-patient relationship, as well as that of parent and child, and the importance of lack of fit between a child and the important people in his life. I'm reminded of your speculative research and your psychical paper, "The Child's Development of the Sense of Reality." I was initially rendered speechless by your penetrating observations about children—their perceptions of the world as they relinquish their fantasies. I have held the idea that children's fantasies are based upon their notions of themselves. I still wonder: How did you know?

Your work remains unfinished. There is so much I want to do. I will write. I will study. I will continue to grow. Today, I pledge to you, as your disciple, though you might not like that word, that I will carry your work forward with all of the possibilities for a better world. I will be your flame. Sándor, my dear friend, you are gone.

When a person I love dies, I want to think of him as happy and fulfilled. Naturally, with Sándor's death, I am in turbulence, reviewing his life with its ambiguities, disappointments, and fulfillments, some of which I am honored to have known intimately. Perhaps his favorite theme was the "'wise baby,' who all at once began to speak from his cradle and spoke so wisely that the grown-ups opened their eyes in astonishment."[18] Such insight, such poetry of expression. He had many qualities of a wise baby and was drawn to the young all of his life. "The academicians of our science did not like him, they feared his élan, regarded him as an enfant terrible." He was aware of this nickname, which hurt him but also made him proud.[19]

The roots of Freud and Ferenczi's clinical differences seemed to arise from their theorizing about very different experiences with patients: the clinical cases of malignant regression with which Freud struggled and those of benign regression wherein Ferenczi courageously joined with the patient. The vitality and, at times, joy with which he conducted his work, his sincerity and ready enthusiasm for new ideas and successful experiments, carried him to his new technique based on his Relaxation Principle. He somehow knew that responding positively to the patient's expectations and needs, once he had learned their true significance, could often change what he thought of as lifeless, drawn-out analysis.[20] Of course, this approach then meant abandoning Freud's principle of abstinence, which required analysts not to respond to a regressed patient's cravings and, in particular, not satisfy them; instead, the analysis must be carried out in a state of abstinence or frustration.

Ferenczi saw the problems raised by his technical innovations, but he fervently believed that his findings, late in his life, amounted to major progress in analytic technique. Right this moment, I am feeling again perhaps the most painful problem for him: Why it was that Freud could not see the importance of these new ideas? I am certain that the feeling of not being understood by Freud hindered him.[21]

Tomorrow, when I speak before the friends and others gathered at his burial, I will put forth the hope that his life's work brought to us and how his relentless search for truth, with its discoveries and disappointments, is his legacy. I will gird myself with the imaginative and luminous words of our circle of friends. I hold Gyula Krúdy's phrase in my mind: "What you have loved remains yours."[22]

Now, at the time of his death, many of us, his closest friends, write passionately about his generous attitude towards us. I know his generosity well. He was a point of convergence for the humanity of the rest of us, where our thinking could be safely exposed, even welcomed. Veigelsberg ("Ignotus"), Karinthy, the great novelist Márai—we are angry, stunned, and saddened at his passing. We are feeling the first blow of an immense personal and collective loss.

My thoughts are scattered about what to say when we gather for the funeral. I am wrestling with commenting on the obvious academic con-

tributions and with the preponderance of the more compelling emotions for Ferenczi which so many of us are suffering. Even at the time that I began composing my thoughts about his contributions, well known by the public and his circle, I am caught by the more personal and ephemeral aspects of his personality—what I received from him. I see from his notes that even at the end, he was delving deeply into himself to understand so many things. He was questioning everything about himself. This eulogy... I want to capture those qualities about him that were strong and rare, those that will continue after him. Sándor, I hope that being in your office can help with my task somehow. Here is what I have written thus far:

> *He was a person of unusual candor, daring to hear expressing personal feelings, unconventional ideas, and intuitive leaps. Neurologist, psychiatrist, psychoanalyst, he was a true physician, most concerned with helping, healing, and the relief of suffering. Ferenczi was Budapest's first psychoanalyst, and he established the Hungarian Psychoanalytic Society in 1913. He was well known and highly respected in the progressive circles of the city's intellectuals. He published essays about the field in* Nyugat *and* Huszadik Szazad. *He was elected president of the International Psychoanalytic Association in 1918, held in Budapest. "Pure gold," Freud said of Ferenczi's writings. Indeed, Kosztolányi described him as "one of the true luminaries in psychoanalysis." Márai stated, "Without the work of Freud and the intellectual refinements and contributions of Ferenczi, one could scarcely imagine the intellectual cross-section of the century." Furthermore, "[with] his new technique, Ferenczi managed to penetrate the human mind to a depth that no one had done before."[23]*

CHAPTER 4

Ferenczi Gathers with the Regulars in Budapest, 1910

I must leave soon to meet my friends at the Café Royal. I can see from my window that Erzsébet-körút is crowded. What is making me pause is my disagreement with Freud. Everything about it is troubling, but this does not dampen my eagerness this morning as I look forward to the company of friends. We'll talk of everything, from politics to coffee service. Everything about this world is remarkable and difficult at the same time. My friends are curious, open, and some are driven by psychoanalytic ideas. I feel a sense of boundlessness to the day, to the city, to my own life. Maybe the conversation will be limitless. I am a professional man, considered warm and friendly, thoughtful. I measure my words, but I feel a sense of abandon with this group. I come to the table with ease and expectation. I am occupied with many ideas, some complexities, some fascinations, and above all, desiring the minds of others. This morning blazes with an intensity of feeling. This is a day like so many others and a day unlike any other. I watch the sky and clouds, the river sliding past in silence. It is only morning, and already I am seized by this need to talk to these friends.

Alone at the table sits the writer Karinthy. Deep in thought, he writes as he waits for three others to arrive:

Everything returns and renews itself. The difference now is that the rate at which these returns occur has increased, in both space and time, in an unheard-of fashion, now my thoughts can circle the globe in minutes. Entire passages of world history are played out in a couple of years.

Something must result from this chain of thoughts.

If only I knew what! (I feel as if I knew the answer to all this, but I've forgotten what it was or was overcome with doubt. Maybe I was too close to the truth. Near the North Pole, they say, the needle of a compass goes haywire, turning around in circles. It seems as if the same thing happens to our beliefs when we get too close to God.)

Stepping up to my table in the café where I am now writing [a man interrupted my chain of thought.] He walked up to me and made me forget what I was going to say. Why did he come here and disturb me? The first link: he doesn't think much of people he finds scribbling. The second link: this world doesn't value scribbling nearly as much as it used to just a quarter of a century ago. The famous worldviews and thoughts that marked the end of the 19th century are to no avail today. Now we disdain the intellect. The third link: this disdain is the course of hysteria and fear and terror that grips Europe today. And so the fourth link: the order of the world has been destroyed.[24]

My friends are gathered at their table. I'm delighted to see four of them already engaged in lively conversation.

Today, I am associating words as I view my close friends. It seems to satisfy something in me to describe them to myself. My eye is first drawn to Kosztolányi. He is a kalcidoscope of attributes: influential, critical, ambitious, loyal, seeks the authentic man, apolitical, the dandy, classical decadence. Then there is Karinthy, who is ambitious, steadfast, flourishing, smoldering, courageous, multicolored, ineffable. Márai has joined our table today—a lustrous, elegant, serious, discreet, passionate, and magnificent man. There is Ignotus, influential, lyrical, quick, steadfast, enigmatic, with deep understanding, a force. Ignotus is my longest and possibly closest friend. He has given me help and courage for everything. He is my forum whose opinion I accept as decisive with almost blind certainty.

Márai, novelist and journalist, brings me deep listening and astute observing. He is a genius of humanity, this friend. He is a man who is as comfortable among his friends in expressing his dreads, dislikes and passions as he is able to write about them in his novels.

Kosztolányi, a sparkling elegant man, is multifaceted and changeable. There is nothing accidental about him as a writer, shifting between genres. A virtuoso in poetry and prose, translator and master of rhyme, many feel that through his writing and translations, he will do the most to develop the Hungarian language in the world.

I am richly nourished by my poet and novelist friends, though I take a direction of my own. Psychoanalysis is not just an idea, it is a way of seeing and a way of understanding. I found a similarity in Kosztolányi's characters, but his characters aren't living people, which interest me the most. I believe there was something in me that Freud called upon. It has been part of me from as early as I can remember, but I didn't have a name for it. When I first met Freud at his home in February, 1908, only four years ago, the event changed my life, like seeds dropping from a sack on a fertile field. I was thirty-five, Freud was fifty-two.

As I take my usual seat at the table, the group is deep in conversation about the forthcoming issue of Nyugat.[25] *I wait in silence, absorbing the atmosphere. What dwells here? A safe place where one can be free, devout, and even worshipful. That mysterious process of living among others. We all need to talk and share it. I need to share it and talk about it. If I don't recapture a feeling, what then? Will it vanish? Will I vanish? This is a place infinite with possibilities. It is a communion.*

From the North and East we await three others—Berény, a painter, and Ady and József, poets. Many of my artistic friends seem drawn to psychoanalysis, this irregular work, partly from intuitive understanding, but also they rebel against scientific scholasticism. I am powerfully drawn to these friends and find myself at home among them. I need these friends. My desire to understand, while poetic and intuitive, is still a desire to understand. Who am I but one who above all wants to be loved, to understand, and to be understood? To remain open and reveal myself is the best way I can imagine to achieve this, but I seem to create a disturbance in others by taking these liberties. I find that I must return again and again to this group who are not frightened by me.

Nyugat published Kosztolányi's colorful narrative, "Budapest, 10 September 1909," which portrayed the atmosphere and friendships in the coffeehouse culture. He described three friends, Kan-

icky, Sarkany, and Esti, as they sat down together at their regulars'
table. At last they were together, the three of them:

> The restaurant was gleaming white. The purple light of
> lamps above the freshly washed cambric tablecloths ap-
> peared to be untouched virgin altars at which nobody had
> taken communion yet. Their connection created a chain
> that linked and their world became complete: their soci-
> ety—the Balkan Society—gathered to exercise the free, brave
> and public of such and similar operations. They were roast-
> ing the afternoon coffee. Its aroma was tickling their nos-
> es. The gallery above, with its twisted and gilded Baroque
> columns, like a Buddhist temple, seemed to be waiting for
> something.
> The coffeehouse was buzzing, the noise in the gallery was
> getting stronger. In this harsh racket they were feeling the
> rhythm of their lives and that they were headed somewhere,
> moving forward. Every table, every booth, was occupied.
> Storm clouds were towering from the (cigarette) smoke.
> It felt good to stretch out in this steamy, warm puddle,
> thinking about nothing, just watching how it boiled and
> bubbled, knowing that those who were splish-splashing in
> it would slowly be slackened, steamed, cooked, concoct-
> ed together into one single bowl of bussing broth. They
> could see their everyday acquaintances, scattered around
> at different tables, on velvet sofas and chairs. They had all
> arrived.
> Here was Bogar, the young novelist.

Playing the piano was Aracsy, the painter, who had gotten himself photographed in a Florentine knight's armor with a dagger on his side.

Here was Beleznay, the famous art collector, a personal acquaintance of Wilde and Rodin.

Here was Szilvas, the "marquis," with an ivory-handled walking stick, an incomparable conversationalist who blended our newest slang words in a humorous and masterful manner with the obsolete expressions used in lexicons on neologisms, archeologists' papers, and inaugural academic speeches.

Here was Elian, the neurologist.

Golya, the applied artist.

Soti, the scientist who studied the origins of our folk tales.

Boldog, the modern photographer.

Here was Dayka, the blonde son of a big landowner, who immersed himself in Neo-Kantianism and talked about epistemology. Here was Kovacs, who never talked but collected stamps and smiled sarcastically.

Here was Mokosay who had already visited Paris, read Verlaine and Baudelaire in the French original, and quoted from the French original, with great enthusiasm and bad pronunciation.

Here was Belenyes, the "sworn chemist," who lost his job because of committing some kind of irregularity and now loitered around editorial offices of newspapers and provided data for investigative reporters.

Here was Kotra, the dramaturge who demanded pure literature. The purest possible literature, on the stage as well, and wanted to stage the drama entitled "Waiting for Death" which was being written by Geza, his friend sitting next to him, and in which there were no humans, only objects, and the key and the keyhole were engaged in a long and deep metaphysical argument with one another. Here was Pirnik, the international Social Democrat. Here was Scartabelli, the aesthetician and polyhistor, who in his warm bass voice discussed partly Wundt and experimental psychology, partly the small streets of Buda, in a highly sentimental manner, emphasizing that he was not sentimental.

Here was Eyssen, about whom no one knew more than the fact he had syphilis.

Here was Bolta, who did not consider Petofi a poet because Jenő Komjáthy was the poet.

Here was Spitzer, who thought that Max Nordau was the greatest mind in the world.

Wesselényi, a high brow assistant pharmacist.

Here was Sebes, who had already two short stories published in daily papers and one that had been accepted.

Here was Moldvai, the lyricist. Here was Czakó, another lyricist. Here was Erdody-Erlauer, a third lyricist.

Here was Valer V. Vandory, the literary translator who translated from every language but spoke none, including his mother tongue.

Here was Specht, the child of rich parents, a modest and shy young man who had not written anything but he had been treated in a lunatic asylum for two years and constantly carried in his pocket a stamped certificate signed by three psychiatrists that he was totally sane.

All in all, everybody was here.[26]

They talked all at once.

About whether or not man had free will; what shape the plague bacterium was, what the wages were in England; how far Sirius was; what Nietzsche meant by "eternal recurrence"; whether or not homosexuality was justifiable; and whether Anatole France was Jewish. They wanted to penetrate into the meaning of everything, quickly and thoroughly, because although they were all young, slightly older than twenty, they felt as if they did not have much time left.[27]

In his book *The Garden and the Workshop*, Hungarian cultural historian Péter Hanák portrayed the cultural upheaval at the end of the nineteenth century:

> Fin-de-siècle artists in Vienna withdrew into their private gardens to tend the gardens of their souls. Those in Budapest, termed newspaper offices, workshops—a phrase coined by the poet Endre Ady—where they found both a refuge and companion in arms. Modernism led to an awareness of existential dangers, in the case of the Viennese, and of the common fate of Hungarians and humanity, in Budapest.[28]

The social milieu of Budapest favored stimulating intellectual battles and the flight into creativity from ever more threatening, destructive trends. Hanák described the main theme of the decade preceding World War I as:

... loneliness, chilling solitude, the severing of the communal transmission lines between communications and understanding—and along with that, and from the same roots, the desire to escape, either into the self, the soul, the tower, or the Garden if you will, the harmony of the garden before the Fall, and the adoration of beauty. [29]

Creative solitude was making its way into the depths of the soul. Babits, Ady, Kosztolányi, and Karinthy all arrived at psychoanalysis, which heralded the recognition and acceptance of ambivalence as the modern form of existence. Resolve was sought in art; there was reverence for beauty. Out of this milieu grew the *Nyugat* generation's euphoria about language, their belief in the magic of the word, and this gave rise to the thesis of Lukács and his circle that artwork is the primary reflection of reality.[30] Literature and art became expressions of cultural tensions and change.

In addition to publishing journals, intellectuals congregated in literary, artistic, and political societies, the best known of which were the Galileo Circle and the Sunday Circle. The Galileo Circle was founded by Karl Polanyi, editor of the group's journal, *Szabad Gondolat* (*Free Thought*). This socialist forum of freethinkers, mostly students, later supported Ferenczi's nomination to a chair of psychoanalysis at the University of Budapest.[31] Ferenczi, a member of the Galileo Circle, gave numerous lectures and published in *Szabad Gondolat*. Many members later became analysts, such as Hermann and Jéno Hárnik.

The Sunday Circle was primarily devoted to the fine arts. Founded in 1915 by sociologist Karl Mannheim and literary critic Lukács, it was a meeting of artists, writers, and musicians, including Béla Bartók. Several members—Rene Spitz, Edit Ludowyk-Gyömorői, and Julia Lang, Mannheim's wife—became analysts.[32]

The *Nyugat* writers were engaged in a cultural battle:

> They struggled against obstacles to writing modernist literature in a Hungarian context, namely a public that was only partially open to their work, and most of all the guardians of establishment culture. The first generation of *Nyugat* set the trend and would eventually become accepted as the best literary journal of the period. Transgression of the cultural norms of the period led to a battle between the *Nyugat* writers and the establishment. The writers often dealt with controversial and erotic themes, as well as other topics unacceptable to polite society, once openly called pornographic by *Magyar Culture*, a conservative cultural journal of the time. Other transgressions committed by the *Nyugat* writers involved the bohemian lifestyle embraced by many of its contributors along with inveterate womanizing and addiction by a few.[33]

In 1924, Kosztolányi wrote a nostalgic poem, "New York Coffee-House," which contained this passage about the deserted New York Café, once the meeting-place of writers in Budapest:

> New York coffeehouse, where I sat often,
> May I enter and sit down for a while,
> Like a beggar who rests on a bench,
> I look and see what has remained of me and around me.
> This summer eve, they are having dinner,

I'd like to drink a cup of coffee at my table,
And like a Christian, I'd even say a prayer,
For the lost youth and for the old fever.[34]

In these meetings, psychoanalysis and literature were intertwined. Psychoanalyst Michelle Moreau-Ricaud described "[a] sort of poets' circle... taking form. Poets and analyst were under reciprocal influence. Ferenczi taught and the writers created. For Ferenczi, the poets' influence was a forum where he tried out his ideas."[35]

Thus, there came to be another presence at the table that Ferenczi brought with him, as if occupying an empty chair at the regulars' table. Like a secular Elijah, Freud was very much there at the table from 1908 onward.

In 1911, Ferenczi reflects on Freud:

To have a confidant in one's life seems imperative. Freud and I have differed on what is held in secret confidence. Secrets are about desire. Shedding light on the truth behind secrets is something I think about. I live in fantasy and imaginative nostalgia about former times where friends could speak honestly to each other. Psychoanalysis, as Freud has invented it, is a pursuit of secrets—the repressed unconscious, while I seek intimacy, true intimacy that may be attainable only in psychoanalysis. I don't know. Freud warned me, "Don't sacrifice too many of your secrets out of an excess of kindness."[36] I cannot tell whether he knows that he is speaking about himself and the secrets he holds in ample supply, secrets that make him ultimately knowable as a confidant. I disturb his perfect silence. Yet I dare not confront him lest he cast me off as he has done to others. The list of cast-offs is legion—Tausk, Jung, Adler, to name only a few. He wants disciples, not friends, and certainly not someone who "sacrifices too many secrets"—his or mine? I have been a fool to ask for intimacy with him, a relationship in which secrets are shared.

I am embarrassed to recall the letters I sent him, but I keep returning to them nonetheless. I cannot let them go. A few stand out as if I only posted them yesterday, not years ago. Particularly this letter of October 3, 1910, which I signed, "thirsty for honesty":

Dear Professor,

I was anticipating your letter with no slight tension—I almost wrote "anxiety." I have already tried to familiarize myself—in fantasy—with all eventualities and even prepared myself for the situation in which, with all respect to the disappointment that I caused you, you will no longer find it worthwhile to be interested in me, etc. My "heroic" plan was to remain loyal to you without consideration for our personal relations, that is to say, for your change of heart.

...What made me inhibited and taciturn—and at the same time somewhat stupid was the same thing you are complaining about. I was longing for personal uninhibited, cheerful companionship with you (and I can be cheerful, indeed, boisterously cheerful), and I felt—perhaps unjustifiably—forced back into the infantile role. To be sure, I did, perhaps, have an exaggerated idea of companionship between two men who tell each other the truth unrelentingly, sacrificing all consideration.

The longing for such a friend and the instinctual impulses that underlie it were not the sole causes of this perhaps irrational fantasy formation. I usually tend more toward modesty and self-deprecation—at least I always see my actual smallness.—But don't forget that for years I have been occupied with nothing but the products of your intellect, and I have also felt the man behind every sentence of your works and made him my confidant. Whether you want to be or not, you are one of the great master teachers of mankind, and you must allow your readers to approach you, at least intellectually, in a personal relationship as well. . . . So I am and have been much, much more intimately acquainted and conversant with you than you could have imagined.

But I believe many other things. I believe that you will in no way misunderstand the tone and content of this letter; I believe that our trip means not the end of intimacy but rather the beginning of a real understanding...

...And If this terribly long epistle were otherwise uninteresting to you it will perhaps interest you as the confession of a man who exists in psychoanalytic ferment.[37]

CHAPTER 5

Attitude Among Corresponding Friends: It Was the Tone

The Ferenczi–Freud struggle was a desire for open dialogue versus a desire for privacy. Both positions appealed to me. Ferenczi was the poet, looking for intimacy in relationships and conversations. I related. I identified with Ferenczi's need.

Ferenczi held that the determining factor in healing and in many different human relationships was the dialogue of the unconscious. For him, the unified, mysterious interconnectedness of two individuals' unconscious minds opened the door to deeper experiences. In his *Clinical Diary*, in 1932, Ferenczi wrote:

> When two people meet for the first time, I said then, an exchange takes place not only of conscious but also unconscious stirrings... Ultimately I meant by this that when two people converse, not only a conscious dialogue takes place, but an unconscious one, from both sides. In other words,

next to the attention-cathected conversation, or parallel to it, a relaxed dialogue is also pursued.[38]

In his review of *The Correspondence of Sigmund Freud and Sándor Ferenczi. Vol I: 1908-14*, Adam Phillips asked the question: "Just what happens when two people choose to speak differently to each other?" His answer: "The world is changed." Ferenczi planned a book on thought transference that he never wrote. He knew about the inextricability of two people that occurs when they speak to each other.[39] We have all experienced this, if even for a few moments: The experience of entering another's mind initiates the transformation of the relationship.

Next follows the desire to engage in a particular kind of conversation. Reading Mary Gluck's *The Budapest Flaneur*[40], I reflected that to be a *flaneuse* is not a choice. It is something that develops autobiographically, naturally, and becomes a different kind of seeing and sensing. One becomes a watcher of people and places, experiencing time by watching the light, seeing the light on the inside and the outside of a person and knowing this about oneself. There was nowhere for me to escape from or avoid this way of being. I could not tell you what I saw concretely, because mostly it was invisible—a nuance, a shadow a tune, a rhythm—sometimes transparent but often seen and heard by noting what was stimulated in me. In meeting and watching someone, I was rarely ever able to recall whether one wore a wedding ring or what the room was like. Instead, I was drawn toward the presence of an underlying story. It was the intangible that I found first. I thought about Bartók pursuing primitive peasant folk music that most agreed had vanished and how, one afternoon in 1904, overhearing a nursemaid cooing a lullaby had reshaped his entire mind! Hearing and sensing a simple peasant tune, he followed the thread:

> Like the apple in the dark mud, he picked up on it, turned it this way and that, and he scribbled down the melody to better understand the shape of this thing he could not yet grasp but in that moment he had discovered his true master.[41]

What were the threads that developed between these habitués of the regulars' tables in the coffeehouses of Budapest and helped them become themselves over several decades of meeting regularly in their communing ritual? These friends wrote very seriously about each other. They responded to each other in print, publishing in *Nyugat* and in their letters, their novels, their psychoanalytic papers, their spoken reactions and ideas, and their gestures of sameness and difference. When one friend would take on a subject, another friend would respond. Kosztolányi and Karinthy had a life-long friendship throughout which they wrote to and about each other's written works and their dialogue was an integral part in the richness of the regular's table conversations. Among the regulars, for example, Ignotus wrote to the poet Ady in *Nyugat* in a piece entitled "Immortal Ady" (1919), and Ferenczi published a letter to Karinthy in *Nyugat* entitled "Anesthetic Science and Alarm" (1924), to which Karinthy responded in the same manner. Kosztolányi wrote about "tact" in his novel, *Kornél Esti*, and Ferenczi wrote about the same topic in his correspondence with Freud and in his papers on technique.

Ferenczi's influence through his communications with close friends, his letters to Freud, and his formal papers raises the question, *Was he a genius of tact?* A possible answer to this is found in a eulogy for Ferenczi written by Ignotus:

> His life was anyway plagued by knowledge of people and his scientific art, through which he saw everyone in every situation, without their walls to guard them... And despite the fact that he was an analyst, despite the fact that he had been analyzed, it was in vain that he trained himself to see the natural as just that: he could hardly see it that way... This made it hard for him to concentrate on what they were in fact saying, since he was primarily paying attention to what was behind whatever it was they were saying.[42]

Over time, these writers' ideas about tact were often emphasized in their work. The youthful protagonist Esti Kornél, featured prominently in Kosztolányi's 1933 novel, *Kornél Esti*, considered tact as his most particular virtue—better than goodness:[43]

> He knew that there is little that we can do for each other, that for the sake of being happy ourselves we are forced to injure others, sometimes even fatally, and that in great affairs of pitilessness is almost inevitable, but for that very reason he held the conviction that our humanity, our apostleship can only be revealed—honestly and sincerely—in little things, that attentiveness, tact and mutual consideration based on forgiveness are the greatest things on this earth.[44]

In his 1924 novel *Skylark*, Kosztolányi again mentioned tact in describing the instinctive understanding of an elderly priest:

This slight, humble soldier of the cross, who had returned to his village to grow old, engulfed by love and goodness, knew exactly what was going on. But out of tact he said nothing, and out of sympathy showed not the slightest sign of interest. He knew the world was a vale of tears.[45]

Ferenczi's friendship with Freud and with his circle of literati could be described as 'corresponding friends'-all involved in writing and responding to each other in letters , essays or publications. Many of them wrote about the bond of friendship or discussed their interpersonal relationships.

Novelist Márai, for example, wrote, in *Embers*, in 1942:

> On male friendships nothing is so rare in the young as a disinterested bond that demands neither aid nor sacrifice. Boys always expect a sacrifice from those who are standard-bearers of their hopes. The two friends felt that they were living in a miraculous and unnamable state of grace... There is nothing to equal the delicacy of such relationship. Everything that life has to offer later, sentimental yearnings or raw desire, intense feelings and eventually the bonds of passion, will all be coarser, more barbaric.[46]

Babits wrote a long necrology about Kosztolányi that was published in *Nyugat* in December, 1936. The entire issue was dedicated to his memory, and some consider it the most beautiful issue in the history of the journal, as the following excerpt demonstrates:

> He grew up very slowly, like a horrific embryo. As if his entire oeuvre would have been simply a preparation for those

last few poems in which this thought ripens and comes to fruition: the idea of death. He loved life in all of its minute details and tiniest slivers. Beyond them he believed in nothing.[47]

In 1924, Ferenczi wrote a tribute to *Nyugat's* editor titled, "Ignotus, the Understanding":

Where is the green lawn I was laying on, listening to your always quick-witted, deeply insightful judgments and predictions about everything and everybody? I will try to recall what the main thing was that I could thank you for in the course of my personal development. I can summarize my impression in one word: it was understanding I received from you. It was no small deal, considering that I was completely alone in the country, representing the most recent approach in the science of the psyche, against a condescendingly disdainful or loudly derisive, sometimes cursing crowd. It was a big thing indeed that, at a time like that, one could come across a person who was able to comprehend in the blink of an eye the depths into which the new approach opened a path for further study, a person who was "only" a poet and a Hungarian writer, but still followed me on my path without hesitation, relying on his keen sense of sniffing and disciplined mind. This path was his path as well since both of us were looking for the Truth. Besides all these, you were also compelled to have an enormous amount of ethical courage to incessantly break a lance for me, the lone fighter, even in front of the public. For me, you became the forum whose opinion I could accept as decisive, with almost blind certainty, and you became the "refined reagent" with which I could test the value of my ideas...

Many years have passed since we had our last argument; both of us have graying hair, but I at least still cannot believe in ephemerality and often believe that the time will come when there will be no events and we will be able to lay on the lawn again together, immersed in weaving new thoughts.[48]

I am dreaming again, silently writing, imaginatively projecting, and floating in and out of past and present. Framed in the café's light at the Hotel Royal are Ferenczi and his friends.

As I sat there, I imagined what transpired—their walk home digesting the experience—and then next time they all met again. What did they think on their next approach to the café? What was catalyzed by the group, how did reflection in solitude affect each one? How did they process and share their writing ideas? Their lives were intertwined over many years, with long-term connections valued. They thought about each other, they wrote about each other. What was going on between them? Before, during, and after? What was their ritual, and did they ever discuss their connection to each other, or did it remain forever unstated, each with his subjective experience held and contained, not explicitly spoken but silently written and then shared later through the others reading what had been written.

I believed that the minds of two of the regulars, Márai and Kosztolányi, were engaged in a mutual influence. When did it happen? Commingling fact and fiction, I imagined conversations among the regulars but also considered the writings of several as they conveyed a deep understanding of human nature. Wading through diaries, novels, and papers, what emerged for me between these friends, expressed separately, in their writing was *tact*. How did this occur? In the moment, while reading and comparing their perspectives, I remember the word startling me in Sándor's expression of his ideas and feelings about psychological tact as an analyst. Today, the understanding of tact may have been lost. I mused as to how, over the years, the contact between these friends, the conversations, the disagreements and agreements created a shared value and concept. None of this was an accident.

Vagabond in my imagination, I lost all sense of time in my absorption, rapidly and tacitly following a thread. I felt the pleasure of searching for what is lost—the intimate experience buried in memories, stories, eulogies, obituaries, hidden and misplaced—searching without horizon, like a flâneuse strolling. Baudelaire described a roving soul in search of a body entering another person's mind whenever he wishes.[49] In 2010, Edmund de Waal wrote about the pleasure of searching, particularly "[the] way you lose your sense of time when you are researching, are pulled on by whims as much as intent."[50] I fantasized about the possibility of having collegial and personal relationships that are truly *free associations*. So, as I watched the regulars' table in 1910, I thought, *They have entered each other's minds*; for I have followed an emotional trail, searching for the feel of mutuality.

Under the spell, the coffee house came alive offering a taste of conversations, a parallel experience from their words, extracted from history, from letters, and writings between friends. What would I carry forward? A distillation of their strong emotions?

These ideas gleaned from Ferenczi's letter to Freud on October 3, 1910[51] stayed with me:

> Someone finding it "worthwhile to be interested in me";
> "... longing for personal, uninhibited... companionship...";
> "... two... who tell each other the truth, *unrelentingly*...";
> "I've felt the man behind every sentence of your works and made him my confidant";
> "... not the end of intimacy but rather the beginning of a real understanding"; and Ferenczi's knowledge that people speaking differently to each other changes the world.

From Ferenczi's (1924a) tribute to Ignotus, I retained these pieces:

> Understanding "in the blink of an eye" the depths to comprehend;
> "... the forum whose opinion I could accept as decisive, with almost blind certainty...";
> "... lay[ing] on the lawn . . . together, immersed in weaving new thoughts";
> "... a person who... still followed me on my path without hesitation";
> "You and Róbert Berény... were like a genuine institution for me," helping to bear the "exclusion" by others; and
> "... we saw the world differently than we had the day before."[52]

Such passion reflected in these companions' words. What could I do to manifest some of this passion in my life? Then I read this paragraph Ignotus wrote in his eulogy for Ferenczi:

Many years later, I can see the two of us sitting in his consulting room one Sunday afternoon when he didn't have patients. We sat side by side, in silence, holding hands with our eyes closed, observing our thoughts, and then each scribbling down on a piece of paper what they had thought, what had come to mind, and, comparing the two scraps we saw that what had come into my mind was associated, by the logic of Freudian dream interpretation, with what Ferenczi had thought of . . . and so I believed in the transfer of thoughts. And so what was going on, in a small way, in the Városmajor and on Erzsébet Avenue, must have been going on throughout the world on a far grander scale—and today, as the new physics has engendered a new view of the world, the new analysis has engendered a new view of the person.[33]

I held my breath and thought: two friends together, writing in silence. Friends who could care and feel in such ways. A friend who would find it worthwhile to be interested in me. Someone longing to have a personal, uninhibited companionship. We would tell each other the truth. Unrelentingly. I want to do that! I want that! It would be a commitment to live in this way. Who would join me? I thought of two different men, nearby in spirit but both living far away. Who lived in my town? This kind of relationship needed to be conducted in person, and with someone who possessed the capacity to sustain an intimate relationship. I didn't want to scare anyone, as Ferenczi had scared Freud and pushed him to their famous ending. Who would not roll their eyes about this or about me later on? Or worse, yawn with boredom while, ironically, I was searching for a *cure d'ennui*. Could there be a kindred spirit? Then it came to me. There was somebody. And as I thought about it more, I'd known he was the person all along.

On September 14, 2012, my new friend and emerging confidant, Colin, joined me in the garden in silence. We held our pens and blank sheets of paper—modern-day dogs' tongues. The setting, time, objects, and light all delivered the aesthetic we craved.

We emulated what we imagined the two friends, Ferenczi and Ignotus, did long ago in the early 20th century in Budapest. Open to whatever the exercise brought us, we wrote together in silence.

> *"We are going somewhere forward."* (Kosztolányi, "Budapest, 10 September, 1909")

> *"We are going somewhere forward."* (Central Coast California, 10 September, 2012)

CHAPTER 6

Silent Writing

We were a man and a woman, each with our own partners. We had a table between us, our paper and pens, and the power of silence. In the beginning, this was comfortable because it was all new. We were contained by conscious knowledge about our lives. No rules. Intimacy between friends. Like a psychoanalytic session, an appropriate vessel to contain everything. A freely chosen association where we didn't need to censor anything. A deliberate invitation to become personal. What we didn't know then was that silent writing wasn't a trip in the known. Barriers would shape-shift and assumptions would change. It was only a matter of time.

There was a moment I realized I felt differently about him—the light, darkness, his pain, and trust, his person. There was also *the gaze*. I cautioned myself, knowing that "the gaze" is about the object of our desire (*objet petit a*) and that behind our desire is nothing but our lack (Lacanian gaze).[54] Despite this trickery, and keeping it in mind, we began to move forward. Or was it backward?

There was a presence about him, a wealth kept inside, quietly watching. Was it his curiosity waiting? And for what? A vein of introspection that he preferred to leave alone? I also watched.

As a door began to open, I entered. An early awareness, too premature for words. Something in exile that I sensed in him and in the possibility of friendship. I was knowledgeable about the familiar and unfamiliar in myself, the roots of the uncanny, or as Freud would say, *das Unheimliche*.[55] To share an experience of the uncanny could be very powerful between us. I was aware of the many names describing uncanny experience: telepathy, thought transference, the intangible emotional connections often referred to as *intuitive*. Also, for me came what the Irish call "secret ear," the *cluas faoi run*, another way of listening that involves experiencing ominous events unfold before they happen in real time. Of course, this "gift" ran in my family, so the myth goes. For Colin and me, less and less did it matter what historic others had written or what was in need of proving and discovering. For a while, we relaxed and forgot about Ferenczi and Ignotus's experimentation with thought transference. Creating our own process, we transcended the impetus of history. *We were in history*. In the spirit of Dada's *cadaver exquis*, a poem written by several poets without knowing what the others had already contributed, we were absorbed in our multiple subjectivities. There was no speaking of these thoughts and emotions. My thoughts were reserved for writing and our silent writing. Never emerging from this fascination, I fell under the spell of its extraordinary presence.

Locating him required silence. Silence permitted the implicit knowing of another person and made space for a hoped-for intimacy that could easily have been lost to the rush of time. Silence summons what is latent between two people.

I needed our silence to be a secret—to be mutually kept. In my memory, few readings in psychoanalytic training gripped as did Masud Khan's famous paper, "Secret as Potential Space."[56] He wrote about the need for his mind to be alive to what he called his patient's *absent self*, a phrase he used to refer to the part of the patient that was held secret in a way that became an act of mutuality. The location of the secret was not inside or outside a person. The person *is* the secret. Our silent writing was another kind of secret. Our co-created process was mutually and exclusively held between us.

We had met 12 years prior. A connection was made, unprocessed by both of us. He went home and mentioned it to his partner, who remembered the specificity of this connection, whereas his recall was vague. I recalled a glimmer of something new and different but also a similar vagueness. He made me laugh by his tone and ironic remarks about abandonment: "always abandonment." Years passed. We were psychoanalysts and attended a group, formed another group, and were involved in a conference. We gradually sought out each other's company.

I knew that he was the only person in my community who would definitely say yes to this experiment. In several discussions, he confessed some reluctance, but over time, his feelings changed, and he moved forward toward the unknown. We agreed there was no need to know the outcome but, instead, only tacit ideas of what might happen. My tendency was to keep possibilities open and avoid being pinned down. I felt it was important to protect myself from a sense of overexposure. His way was to be less defended and generous about the telling of personal experience. He seemed more cavalier about self disclosure than I was.

We met in the late afternoon or evenings, alternating weeks—one garden then another, one living room and then the other.

We would greet one another, laugh and express some quick emotion, a question about red or white wine. Structure and details emerged. We had blank, unlined paper. Pens. We sat across from each other, looking out at the garden, able to glance at one another and also have privacy. Alone in the presence of another, said Winnicott.[57] We wrote steadily and silently. We knew when to stop without a word being said.

We knew instinctively not to analyze or talk much about our process or what we had written. It was too early in the process to know what we were doing. We did not know what we were doing. At the end of the first meeting, after finishing writing, we handed over the pages we had written. We took each other's pages home and kept them carefully. We then read each other's notes, but not the collection of our own pages. The other held them in trust.

With an historic moment in mind, based on *Notes and Fragments—Sándor Ferenczi, 1930-32*, written by Balint after Ferenczi's death, I questioned myself: *What becomes of our pages should something happen to one of us?* The pages contain so much of what is never shared with anyone! Upon Ferenczi's death, a number of notes were found among his papers. These were jottings of ideas for his private use, written in the four languages, fragments which served as the medium of his thinking. They were scribbled on odd bits of paper using abbreviations for phrases and ideas that Balint needed to decode in order to understand his work fully.[58]

A few times in the first and second year of silent writing, Colin and I read *Eulogy by Ignotus*. How intensely Ferenczi and Ignotus sat together, holding hands, passing notes back and forth. Whatever became of their notes? A mystery. They were fascinated with thought transference, an idea that stood out among the many exciting ideas of their time. For a while, we, too, laughingly, semi-seriously, talked about pursuing the idea of thought transference and related anomalous experiences that many others have had. We occasionally read or referred to other writings. Spontaneously, at a conference, we went to a sidewalk psychic, paid the fee, had our palms read, took a photo, laughed and wanted to believe, and forgot about it. A few years later, we returned to the same psychic. Again, we laughed, but not as much, for so much had changed.

In silent writing, the experience of time and the relationship between past, present, and future are broken. One has an awareness of not enough time. I look with a new eye at a growing stack of reading that I will not be able to experience. There isn't time for it. I must learn to discriminate among experiences: ones I desire and those less essential.

I have come to crave the ritual communion of our silent writing. I like to imagine the tones of the past moments, a season remembered by the effect of the light on the roses. As I glance about in a break from written thought, a rare species of butterfly interrupts the catharsis. If this moment in time were encased in amber, what would it be? Something ordinary, yet extraordinary. Looking through a prism at the silent writers reveals the felt intensity, concentration, hazily remembered facial expression and the changing tone as the writing transforms a difficult emotion of the other into calm.

In subtle ways, strange things happened between us over the first three years. There was a period where the compulsivity of another was tormenting him. He would remark ruefully in his writing, "compulsivity wins the day." He would call his marriage off. When life was about compulsivity, was this desire for other a desire gone awry or was it a real absence of something? I felt his painful emotions as he struggled with this difficult challenge. I held the tension, silently resisting the compulsion to analyze. He would have a loving dream about his father and write about it. Simultaneously, I wrote about "father hunger" from the perspective of a husband's shadow of loss.

Secrets. Everything we wrote about and what was happening between us felt secret. We both loved secrets, but I loved them more. He wanted to tell all, or so he said. Yet, I noticed a capacity for discretion and selection, that tact in him that was so important in Freud's relationship with Ferenczi. For me, an ongoing theme in conversation showed up also in my writing: " 'I don't want to talk about it,' I remarked emphatically!" Aware of my ambivalence about disclosing my secrets as opposed to his willingness to do so, I often wondered about fear. When I wrote in silence, I was free to confess my fears and trusted that he possessed an appreciation for the hidden parts of me.

It was easy to become mutually immersed in this process, as I possessed romantic sensibilities similar to the literati's during the fin de siècle. Thought transference was occurring between me and the Hungarian regulars, through their writings and my imaginative projections. Tangential to this, about a year before silent writing began, my mother handed me a book to read, as she often did. Upon reading it, she had thought of me, she said. I put it aside, forgetting it on a shelf, until one day I picked it up and looked at the cover. I saw a sepia-toned background, with a woman standing out from the darkness. Glancing at the printed words, slowly reading, I smiled deeply, comprehending my previous knowledge of the author, a friend of Ferenczi. The book was *Embers*, by Márai, a First Vintage International edition originally published in Budapest, 1942.[59] With this appearance by one of the

Budapest regulars, I thought about what was being illuminated, and I thought about magic.

Sometimes, I worried about loss. Like the fear Kosztolányi expressed in *Skylark*: "When people go away they vanish, turn to nothing, stop being, they exist only in memories, haunting the imagination."[60] Vanishing haunted me. There was nothing to do about absences. Nomadism and traveling for Colin and I were a reality. We shared the strong desire to travel geographically. We loved experiencing different cultures and being away; it was essential to our lives. However, through silent writing, I traveled in my mind and identified with a nomadic state psychically. Nomadism has been said to be the key to psychoanalysis itself, understood as a journey in which the psychic identity itself is reconstituted. I mused about time and wondered whether there was a sense of timelessness or some variation, while writing silently in the presence of another. For these few moments, I do not experience time. It is something else.

All that has occurred and is still rushing forward is contained in an instinctive trust, part intuitive and part daring.

Now I continue in my imagination, aware that I am in a favorite state of reverie. I cannot believe I am so fortunate as to have a trusting friend at this table who takes this seriously and can also laugh with me—at us. I think of the many conversations we have had with another important group gathered around this table. I note my dog, at ease around him and among these friends, his snapping and eating the bees, and I wonder about the ideas and feelings being exposed, opening vulnerabilities in the moment. The sound of single birds blending with a chorus of delicate birdsong make me lazier in my writing, a fade in and fade out experience. I return to the page where my hand holds a pen, and

I re-read something amusing. Continuing, I watch closely as the tree branch shadows spread across the lawn and the multiple roses with orange, salmon, and golden petals draw me to an emotional memory, and I write about this. I ask myself if I am now old? I notice the subtle effects of the drought, things need watering, and friends need nurturing. And then two hummingbirds, ruby-throated species, join another, an Allen's orange-red, on the white, purple, and magenta sages. An abundance in the garden vortex. In the absorption, we can enjoy timelessness. Suddenly, something breaks my dream. and my friend is saying he's done. I realize that I am as well. We exchange our writing. He will go home, I will continue, we will attend to the other parts of our lives, but for a few stolen moments after he leaves, I will relish reading his silent writing... the notes and fragments from our minds. I will often find something that makes me laugh out loud, amidst the seriousness. I'll also realize that being known—the experience of two minds being together, creating understanding—is one of the most powerful things we can experience in life with someone. And I think of one of the old regulars, Márai, on the experience of friendship: "The two friends felt that they were living in a miraculous unnamable state of grace."[61]

Their stories are a force of emotion, alive through their letters, tributes, articles, eulogies. I carry the transfer of their emotion, their stories, and the force of this expression between friends. I can't help but wonder whether this intimate expression began in silent contemplation, in silence, through writing to one another about one another. It tells their story of longing for more of the experience of what they were feeling for each other, with each other.

I don't remember at what point during the beginning of silent writing I sought out Elizabeth Lloyd Mayer's *Extraordinary Knowing*,[62] but it was a gestalt force in the background as Colin and I silently wrote. Her carefully researched, conceptual exploration opened a possibility to consider, without the need to prove or predict a different kind of knowing. I was familiar with intuitive experiences and the kind of connection that is different than any other, such as the common example of thinking about someone who then calls. Another example is feeling "out of the blue," that something is wrong with another person and one of us will call. I can always name the person with whom such experiences happen frequently and with whom an intuitive connection is a fundamental dynamic in our relationship. Broaching certain uncanny subjects, one enters hesitantly. The actual writing and discussion of "the uncanny" automatically increases prefacing, as I am now. We are conditioned to be judged and dismissed if we shift away from rational scientific into radical thinking. The taboo is powerful, especially about this quality of connectedness.[63]

It is essential to understand that it is one's personal experience that initiate curiosity in psi-experiences such as thought transference. As psychotherapists or psychoanalysts, we have all had conversations with clients about the meaning of these kinds of uncanny experiences in their lives. This can be a sensitive topic for some, who reveal their experience carefully; others may have a confident belief in their uncanny connections. Mayer's 14-year journey of writing began with her personal experience of relying on a psychic expert and its significance for her, struggling with her own skepticism about a different variety of knowing than the knowing that is called rational.

I have no interest in providing scientific evidence of the intuitive/psychic experience or predicting something in the future. More interesting and important to me, as it was to Mayer, is the question of whether we are simply being confronted with one more realm of ordinary human psychology. That realm is taboo because it appears to be anomalous; its implications cannot be integrated into familiar psychological or scientific models. The realm of weird experiences with others is beyond our capacity to comprehend or even describe. As Ferenczi kept reminding Freud, it is a realm that lies beyond the limits of scientific inquiry. I am a psychoanalyst that also practices forensic psychology. As experts testifying in court, those of us in this field are trained to avoid referencing our gut instinct, intuition, hunches, or feelings. We must be factual, rational. Yet many of us have relied on our intangible, intuitive knowing and the power of the nonverbal in fleshing out the cunning sadist or the psychopath's mimesis of empathy. This spark has often shown us the way and provided an essential path toward discovering their hidden personality factors.

Colin and I had embarked on an experiment in the uncanny as we freed our minds through writing. Whether it was the residue of the day, a dream, or debating something, the ritual of silence was a powerful dimension for our mutual existence. We wrote frequent questions to each other about thought transference. Was it happening for us as time passed? We wondered about Freud's definition of thought transference as functioning like a telegraph[64] and whether unconscious transmission was contributing to a mystical unification of our psyches. We believed the interconnectedness and permeability of our minds was the core to thought transference.

In the company of psychoanalytic pioneers, we experienced the power of silence as in the consulting room, but our variation and context was a contemporary experiment.

> Sigmund Freud said in explaining the concept of the uncanny that psychoanalysis is not meant to run through the known. It is not an organized trip in the known. It is meant to explore and experience new territories and therefore, to explore uncanny phantasies. In psychoanalysis uncanny phantasies are welcome.[65]

Ferenczi, Freud, and Jung each had lifelong interests in spiritualism and related occult phenomena. Psychoanalytic problems related to the unconscious and altered states of consciousness fueled Ferenczi's interest in spiritist phenomena. Spiritualism and Spiritism comprised "a philosophy, religion and practice based on the supposition that the human soul is independent of the body and thus does not cease to exist after the death of the body."[66] For most psychoanalysts of his day, at the core of spiritualistic phenomena was thought transference. Ferenczi's understanding of thought transference as a "dialogue of the unconscious… pointed at several technical challenges of psychoanalysis and highlighted the questions of countertransference in particular."[67] With his ideas on the flexibility of the borders of the psyche, his emphasis on intersubjectivity in and beyond the analytic situation, and his openness to experiment, Ferenczi undertook a pioneering role in Hungarian psychical research and contributed his theories to the Budapest School of Psychoanalysis.[68]

From Budapest, in a letter dated June 23, 1913, Ferenczi praised Freud's provisional summation of *Totem and Taboo* as Freud's "new and outstanding idea of transmission by means of unconscious understanding."[69] Ferenczi wrote:

> We may safely assume that no generation is able to conceal any of its more important mental processes from its successor. For psychoanalysis has shown us that everyone possesses in his unconscious mental activity an apparatus which enables him to interpret other people's reactions, that is, undo the distortions which other people have imposed on the expression of their feelings. An unconscious understanding such as this... may have made it possible for later generations to take over their heritage of emotion.[70]

Ferenczi's interest in the occult goes back farther than his correspondence with Freud reveals. He became interested in psychoanalysis through Jung's association experiments. Possibly, he hoped to gain a better understanding of the occult through psychoanalysis. "Spiritism," his first scientific paper, written in 1899, reveals the origin of his interest. Freud and Ferenczi were fascinated with thought transference and the occult. Their mutual fascination is reflected in the letters between them. Ferenczi pursued the experience via psychic consultations in Paris and Budapest. Ferenczi visited a medium, Frau Seidler, upon Freud's endorsement, with the intention of investigating parapsychological phenomena. Freud and Ferenczi corresponded about the experience, and after initially counseling Ferenczi to "keep quiet about it for the time being," in his next letter to Ferenczi he insisted, "Let us keep absolute silence about it."[71]

In 1899, in "Spiritism," Ferenczi wrote of psychology as being a science in its infancy:

> The way the mind deals with sense perceptions and feelings, the primitive links it establishes through associations and apperceptions, these are the chapters of the best psychological works of our day. The psychology of love, hate, rage, memory, knowing, forgetting, thinking, moral and artistic sense, the psychology of nations and infants, all this is left to the imagination of dreamers or novelists.[72]

With reference to Mayer's ideas, Philip Bromberg, in his book, *The Shadow of the Tsunami*, discusses the development of the relational mind:

> Elizabeth Lloyd Mayer, in a volume that could well hold the future of psychoanalysis between its covers, expands the phenomenon of intersubjectivity into the domain of what she calls anomalous experience: veridical perceptions that are not compatible with what we classify as rational.[73]

Mayer speaks of the emergence of anomalous perception as a "dissociative jolt":

> A model that aims to contain anomalous cognition has to take into account the feeling of what happens. It has to make room for that unique dissociative jolt, the shock of body, the emotion, and idea erupting into consciousness

65

with knowing that feels utterly different from ordinary knowing. The feeling of what happens is part of the data.[74]

She further comments, "Leaving rational thought behind, even momentarily, isn't a loss we easily invite. But if we want access to the state in which anomalous knowing might be possible, a deliberate invitation might be precisely what is required."[75]

Mayer's explicit argument is that the future of human mental development is not only relational but also intersubjective in ways that go beyond what we now can rationally accept as possible. Bromberg observes that Mayer touches the heart of what underlies human growth in its broadest sense—"the increased ability to stand in the spaces between self-states that would otherwise be alien to each other."[76] Drawing on physics, he also links quantum entanglement to this ineffable interconnection between entities and then quotes Mayer:

> To see a view of the world in which anomalous experience happens, we need to temporarily abandon a view of the world in which rational thought happens. Worse, we need to temporarily abandon the state of mind in which we see what rational thought helps us to see. And vice versa. Refusing to undergo either loss means refusing the possibility of seeing what the other side sees... If people on both sides stay lodged in states of mind from which they can't see what the other insists is perfectly visible, why should either side hear the other's truth as reflecting anything but a matter of faith? Why should either find the other's truth remotely plausible?[77]

In 2001, Mayer published Robert Stoller's paper regarding a series of dreams of his own and his patients that he reluctantly called *telepathic*. She reported that in "Telepathic Dreams?" he discussed how empathy, affective attunement, and other forms of human connectedness by their nature cannot be adequately captured by objective science in terms of their possible relations to anomalous forms of human perception. The notion of telepathy bears upon the question of how one mind comes to know another. Getting to know the mind of another is precisely the business of the psychoanalyst.[78] Mayer comments:

> In a number of ways, then, I anticipate that our growing focus in psychoanalysis on the intersubjective nature of the analytic relationship, will open up other investigations leading us to a better understanding not only of conventional intersubjective reality, but also of the less conventional, certainly equally intersubjective, sphere of "telepathy" and other possibly anomalous perceptions... The point is simply that the articulation of intersubjectivity has promoted an atmosphere of greater technical flexibility that may facilitate the joint investigation of *any* communication.[79]

Holding the incompatible, the conflicted experience, the paradox in a single state of awareness needs a deliberate invitation. The regulars' table was the experience of many creative minds being together. I remember noticing the group process around the table of my friends and that what I was looking for was occurring. I knew it would happen because it felt like the right combination of people. In the midst of our vitality, my reflective process removed me from the group. Knowing that I had arrived, in that very moment, my dissociation began. I had to do it, if only for a few minutes, in order to realize what was occurring.

For Colin and me, silent writing was the specificity of two minds being together. After our third year of writing together, we sensed a nebulous feeling in our process. We discussed what might be changing between us. There wasn't a way to know where we were, whether in the middle or the beginning. We had differing thoughts about the need to define silent writing in a temporal sense. We were experiencing the ambiguity and disorientation that occurs in the middle of ritual, when we felt we were no longer the people we had been but had not yet completed the transition to another "place" in which to live. Approaching the threshold, we were in liminal space. Liminality was the in-between stage between our past ways and the unknown new ways of developing together. It was an ambivalent and uncomfortable position. I was acutely aware of our differences in the ways we tolerated this ambivalent space. I wanted this ritual of communion to remain open, unanswered, and mysterious, because it was sacred. At times, Colin wasn't concerned by these changes and endured my low frustration tolerance. We stood at the threshold between known identity in known time and a new way of being. I felt that we must not lose the inspired history of Ferenczi and Ignotus that we were carrying forward. Though I tried to suppress my fears about the unforetold consequences of vanishing, they hovered in the distance. Uncertain and equivocal, I didn't want to extinguish my desire forever. I hoped for new possibilities. These were the objects of my desire, reflecting the lack in myself. Mortality exposed, I welcomed unconscious fantasy and the opportunity to thrive in this openness to unexpected experience.

Desire led me to the stories of the regulars' table and silent writing. I suspected there were two stories, Colin's and my own, occurring in silent writing. But what story were we in together?

What kind of a story was my silent writing telling? It had come to me from the past, through a eulogy for a friend, written long ago.

Then, I knew it was a love story, after all.

CHAPTER 7

Broken Heart, 1910

The vacation this time is very important to me as well. The last two summers I, too, did not have the fairy-tale feeling of living in freedom and beauty.

—Sigmund Freud[80]

The vacation plans interest me very much. I will study the map and measure off the temporal and spatial distance between Holland and Sicily. My first concern is to spend as few days as possible alone, i. e., not in your company. I will cook up something: maybe a meeting on the way.

—Sándor Ferenczi[81]

I will bring along a very interesting case *of circular alternation of sadism and masochism* for the trip.

—Sándor Ferenczi[82]

The trip in the fall is the main object of my daydreams, which I catch myself at during some of the more monotonous analyses. I, too, am beginning to count the days. Unfortunately, I have too many of them!

—Sándor Ferenczi[83]

Last summer together in Berchtesgaden, the most mean-
ingful one I have ever experienced.

—Sándor Ferenczi[84]

On the 33-hour train trip to join Freud, Ferenczi reflects:
*Time flew by so quickly because of the pleasure in con-
versation with you. Later, I felt lonely in Budapest without
someone to talk to. From that point on, I couldn't help myself from
showering you with my letters. We had been exchanging correspondence regarding daydreams, fantasies and your "Creative Writers and
Day-Dreaming." Yes, I do see how one deceives oneself in fantasy, as
in the dreams, so completely about the value of one's thoughts. In that
letter, I remember my own sense of vanity and determined to overcome
it and send you the letter anyway.*[85]

*Now en route to see you in Sicily, I am aware of my great hope in
anticipation of traveling with, working with, and, in a sense, living with
you, a man whose mind has changed everything for me. How is it that
you chose me to accompany you? Yet I know through our early correspondence, and first meeting that we share the excitement of a future in
a new era—what the analysis can bring to mankind. I'm thinking about
what you said about me in July about doubting that a person like me
could develop himself. You see something in me that gives me so much
hope about myself and perhaps our development together as personal
friends and collaborators.*

*I have 33 hours between Budapest and Leyden, Netherlands. This time
has a way of expanding for me so that I can think freely while traveling
toward our meeting. Since when have I had such a luxurious amount of
time, unencumbered and alone with my own thoughts? The train travel*

has given me the time to think about your reactions to our conversation about thought transference. We must discuss thought transference and Spiritism. I wrote to you that I was a little frightened that you view my observations on thought transference as proven. Feelings of uncertainty and desire have been aroused in me regarding this controversial topic of occultism, but we have time, though, to think about the things' fate.[86] *I realize we both share the interest in thought transference but I know you are rather ambivalent. I know that between us, we are open to the experiment and experience of the psychics, yet I sense some reluctance on your part to write and work together publicly. I want to share with you some impressions from the thought transference experiments conducted with my closest friend, Ignotus. We meet in my office each Sunday afternoon in Erzsébet-körút. He, as you know, is a great supporter of the new ideas in psychoanalysis appearing in Nyugat. I calm myself with the faith that we will have time to talk of this and so much more.*

I am looking forward to more discussion and work on Schreber, and want to understand your view and deep fascination with paranoia.[87] *I want you to understand my thinking as well on this man. On the Schreber matter, I see that your writings and interest in Leonardo da Vinci and Schreber can be attributed to their unique minds and both having risen to levels of competence in their fields. Though you have neither met nor analyzed them, emotionally they represent themes (homosexuality, paranoia) which deeply preoccupy you. These two men seem to be a source of fascination and pleasure. Your previous interest in paranoia, with your female patient, I have discussed with you. Through Schreber's memoirs, you carry on this thematic interest. You are inspired when you call him "wonderful." You did remark jokingly that he should have been made a professor of psychiatry and director of a mental hospital. He was an inmate a few times in the Leipzig Psychiatric Clinic; nevertheless, we will agree, he is a man of demonstrated competence and achievement. I* know you are bringing with you Schreber's Memoirs of a Neuropath.[88] *Your enthusiasm for learning and exploring moves me and I want to share and work together further when we arrive in Sicily.*[89]

Still I am thinking about your need for a "fairy-tale feeling of living in freedom and beauty" which you have not had for two summers. The desire to live in freedom and beauty... I am carrying that idea within me these 33 hours on this train trip. So many thoughts in my mind, yet I drift, even romantically, to imagined scenes between us as intimate friends, with the freedom to converse safely, talking without inhibition, with exquisite interest and understanding. This would be my indulgence... the mind of another and the personal relationship. I want to experience unconditionally, through you, the beauty of Italy, which for you is beyond the visual. The beauty is to be found in the historical layers. I want to acquire sensitivity to those aspects. I feel I need to talk about my largely unarticulated concept of beauty and, by doing so, understand yours more fully. Sicily, you have said, is the most beautiful part of Italy, a place to which you have traveled many times before this. You have said that Sicily's preservation of unique fragments of the Greek and Roman past has captured your thinking into layers. You have studied and visited Italy and been drawn to Greek and Roman history and also to the domination of Sicily by Spain and eventually the Saraceni, the Moors. You have talked of indulging your passion for Magna Graecia, in particular, the archeological remains. This and, I imagine, Syracuse will be important destinations for you and for us both, physically and mentally. I look forward to more illumination from your archeological passion. The main object of my daydreams is almost here. I want so much, and I feel I might be close to having it.

At the time of our trip to Palermo, my ideas about the renewal of the individual and the development of the person, I attributed to be the result of an interaction in our relationship that was without restrictions. I tried to explain the not-quite-understanding between both of us about your maturity and my infantility. I did try to convince myself that you were obviously intellectually old and I was, at least, a very happy youthful child, but it didn't work. I soon recognized that you do not fully appreciate my attitude, good will, and longing for recognition.[90] What I didn't know, could not know, was that you, with your very different ideas and dreams, and I would clash and rupture, changing everything.

You were relentless in your research, consulting with many, including meeting with Carl Jung and Eugen Bleuler in 1909. Your encounter opened up the opportunity for our trip to Palermo. We would travel together in the next year.

I expect I will write pages of unbroken conversation/dialogue. I am infused with a new vision of man, a utopia of the analyzed man. My vision can be realized in relationship with other liberated men, through psychoanalysis, where all of our discussion will be transparent to each other. I hope to do this together.

I approach Palermo by sea, the wide sweeping bay, Conca d'Oro, golden shell, and the brooding presence of Monte Pellegrino. Freud has arranged a three-room suite in the Hotel de France in Piazza Marina and, in Siracusa, the Hotel des Etrangers, which faces the fountain of Arethusa. A luminous sea view from the window with fragrant oleanders. (They are poisonous.)

The world stops. It is moments like these that I live for, similar to when I approach the cafe table in Budapest at the Royal or the New

York , where everything stops and I realize that I don't want to go anywhere else. It is at the café where all the barriers and trouble that the mind makes for itself fall away, and what's left is this sweet, hopeful understanding of our broken, glorious lives. Italian lighting, ravishing surfaces, luminosity. The complexity of this inheritance of visual history overpowers me. In the art, one layer of paint over the other creates ravishing surfaces whose luminosity mimics the layering of schist stones. I am seduced by the translucency of these objects carved in marble.

"Carving is easy, you just go down to the skin and stop."—Michelangelo

Freud is so passionate in his interests. He dominates often without concern for our communication as he cannot but help to follow the impulses of his mind. I am merely tracking his brilliance, and yet I have passion as well. We will work together here in Palermo. He wants to discuss Schreber's famous work on paranoia, Memoirs of a Neuropath, *in collaboration with me. I cannot believe we have arrived and are here setting out to begin this task. I am finally ready to begin all I have imagined. I am full of a beautiful emotion, that I could be so fortunate in this moment.*

I walked into the room and hesitated. I was uneasy in his presence. This first evening of our work, Freud's glance, his body, and his tone gave me pause. He wanted to dictate something to me. I could see in a split second, how at variance we were in intention. What was happening?! One hundred years collided in that pause.

Out of the window, the glass ocean surface changed to textured creviced skin, the cracks visible beneath, the azure coloring draining from its body, leaving it achromatic. I heard odd music in my head, and minor chords clashing with dissonance. The hopeful state I was in leaned precariously, then folded in on itself, undulating at a dangerous angle, out of control. I felt as if I was empty and would implode. I felt unprotected in the face of this destruction. The scaffolding of my desire fell, ancient, in a flash, like centuries of Sicilian earthquakes creating layered images of collapsed towns. Edifices, art to dust. How my heart fell, aware of the monuments, stone carvings, and art I wanted to share with him, all now in ruins.

Crestfallen and with darkness in my soul, I emerged from the rubble. The vain naiveté of my desire betrayed me. I had cared too much for what I desired. My psychic gaze had been solely about what I lacked. Suspended and wounded, I found my character at the moment of his first blow. My whole self rose up to speak from this pause in the storm.

Gravely conflicted in our assumptions, I stood in a burst of rebellion against his authority and said that this was not a collaboration as I had hoped. He was astonished and shocked me with his response: "So this is what you are like? You perhaps wanted to take the whole thing?" My body was hit by shock. I was left out in the cold. Bitter feelings constricted my throat. In that moment, everything collapsed, all had changed and would change everything between us. I felt it in the room, in the space between us. I was reeling with the unbearableness, all the while amidst the glorious beauty of Siracusa.

He worked alone every evening from then on. Of course, with exception of my strong outburst, all of this was private turmoil. I did my best to obscure and hide my disappointment. Later, I knew the meaning of this working alone in the evenings and what this constriction of throat signified: I wanted... to be loved by Freud.[91]

This exotic trip deeply influenced Freud for at least two years afterwards. In Freud's correspondence from the island, he wrote to his wife Martha, "The fundamentally archeological desire of the Sicilian journey can be read: 'The temple of Segesta... was a wonderful vision in deeply solitary and lonely space.'" Freud's Sicily had the same emotional impact for him as it had eight years before in Naples. From Palermo, he wrote again to his wife, "Palermo is an unheard of pleasure... Such a splendor of colours, smells view—and wellness I've never had all at once."[92]

Clearly, we are men on two different journeys of passionate intensity discovering a deep variance of expectation and hope. He wants to advance his life's work, as The Master. For me, this was and will remain the unanticipated collision, rupture, and residue of broken dreams. I find myself preoccupied with secret lamentations. I felt infantile in my longings for his personal attention and interest. I felt in that moment, by the window with a sea view, a death blow. I tried to endure its initial impact. Grappling with emotion, I tried to understand, since I could not be met.

Returning to Budapest, I am faj—hurt. I am in turbulence, wrestling with emotions that course through my body. My heart hurts; my mind is trying to compensate for this shock, yet in my body and soul, I feel something pulsing through my veins. I cannot take in the sunlight, as if my body cannot absorb something essential from my experience in that beautiful, exotic place. Something is affecting me deep inside. I am in a battle with death, on a cellular level, yet I have so much to learn and so much to do.

This strange feeling cannot dominate. I will use my mental powers, my mind, to go forward and carry on. How to live? How to go on? The need to go on. Disillusionment. The beautiful days spent in your company. I can hold on to them. I search for memories of you that are warm and friendly. I don't want to remember our time together negatively, in extensive self-criticism and denigration, although I admit to having this inclination. Blinded by my own sensitivities, I feel I must keep my private anguish hidden. I want to heal, yet am lost in self-pity and grieving. Holding this tension. Something inside tells me to use this emotion for something that has unknown potential. How I respond, engage, and wrestle with this disturbing experience will mark the future of my work. Am I really the enfant terrible? The anticipated and hoped for love, smashed, extinguished. How to reconcile the betrayal? Over time. My desire and hope was so strong that I could not fathom reality's remoteness. Its mysteriousness. Its elusiveness.

The long train ride back to Budapest will give me the time and space to consider and endure what has happened.

Dear Professor, How can I remain loyal to you without consideration for our personal relations, that is to say, for your change of heart? I want to prove to you that I can withstand being thwarted in my good intentions towards you. Perhaps through our correspondence. Despite my personal desires for a friendship, I do feel a closer acquaintance with you and that my general psychic and intellectual development has benefited from this trip to Sicily. I am longing for personal, uninhibited conversation.

Am I idealizing companionship between us, men who tell each other the truth... between two like-minded people? The ideal I was looking for: I wanted to enjoy the man, more than the scholar, in close friendship. The hours of our trip that I value the most are the times in which you divulged personal information about your life. Those were the moments, separate from scientific scholarship, which matter the most.[93]

Why did you only want a certain level of emotional depth and emotional involvement from me? Could it be I asked for more than you were willing to give? I am confused by the unspoken feeling between us. Did I misread your desire? You had limits, while I had none.

Carrying. What is it, then, that needs to be carried forward? When I cannot get what I desire, how do I carry this and live openly, with richness? My work, my legacy can grow out of the disappointment.

Privately, I go back and think through our correspondence before the Sicily trip where I wrote to you. I see these letters as the beginning of a love that inspired me to want more. I was realizing my excited feelings and sharing these beginnings with you. I even caught myself singing a Hungarian song from the 17th century: "On the great ball of earth, no one so orphaned as I."[94] *You said to me once in Berchtesgaden: "Man must love something." What I have in my personal life is something, but it is not enough. It makes me think that Jung was right in his urging me to surround myself, gather young men around me whom I can teach and perhaps also love somewhat. In reading this letter, I see that I have said, "For the time being, allow me to attach such a large portion of libido for you."*[95] *I also felt tactless in weighing you down with such purely personal matters.*

A decade has past, and I have found someone to trust and share the story of Palermo and my feelings of disappointment. I find myself in a most unexpected and fulfilling relationship with you, Groddeck. You are a kind and unpretentious man, who has helped me as a true physician and has become my friend.[96] I have never been able to be so open with another man, not even Sigmund Freud. You have been treating me for my awful nights full of symptoms that make me feel despairing of the future, as if I'm staring death in the face. These thoughts make me feel both uneasy and hopeful; uneasy because I have wanted to suppress my memory and grief over the Palermo incident with Freud and believe that I have worked through the disappointment to have a more mature relationship with him. I am hopeful because I have your friendship and counsel. I also have my friendships with Ignotus and the others, who have made all the difference. All of that said in a heartfelt way, I cannot get away from the impression that the deciding moment in my adult life, held within myself, gave rise to my unresolved psychosomatic issues, for which I have a great confidence in your treatments at Baden Baden.[97]

Many years have passed since Palermo, and I am fatigued by illness. Since that turning point, I have continually worked hard to surmount the obstacles in all of my important relationships that prevent the most desirable of communications—the personal. Whenever I pause and think about the beautiful times and place in Sicily, I think of the heart and tenderness, delicate psychic tissues that are left deep within yet remain present and vulnerable. Then, I think of a paragraph that erupted out of me, a note fragment I wrote, then tore up. Yet it is etched in my

memory exactly as if it occurred yesterday. I think of that moment of realization, looking out of the hotel window in Palermo at the sea, and I feel the shattering:

> And then in a single sentence, you said the words that began the shattering. The fault line cracked, ever so slightly, and widened a fraction during each subsequent encounter until, one day, it engulfed and drowned my hope. All of my life, I will always remember, with a full heart, my beginning feelings of love and your fatal remark, which changed it all and took away the possibility of beauty.

CHAPTER 8

Finger of God

Reveries are valuable. I often imagine another time or place, a different (or truer) life, perhaps in another time or century. A romantic can feel melancholy about reality while simultaneously aware of what could be and what is impossible. Through imagination, she is sustained by a hope of her longings being fulfilled. Longing is haunting, painful, and ancient, relentlessly stirring up hope. It is a life sentence. A romantic may be criticized for her dreaminess, dismissed for her foolish imagination, derided for her suffering, yet it is a fate she cannot choose. Given that sentence, I decided to pursue what I wanted, no matter how impractical or absurd. I wanted it.

A deep desire for friendship led me to Budapest. I was drawn to this close-knit group of comrades in fin-de-siècle Budapest who challenged conventional thinking, these intellectuals on the fringe. Psychoanalyst Ferenczi and his literati friends were each other's constant companions. I wanted context for The Regulars' Table project. I wanted a sense of "what was" and "what could be" between enduring and deeply attached friends like the "Budapest type."[98] I thought of Georg Groddeck's "it," our relationship with the unconscious, where forces guide us and allow for the mysterious experience and the risk in that. I consumed it between Ferenczi and his regulars in their writings. I wanted to understand these

Hungarian friends, and I wanted this type of relationship, in my town and in my life.

The plans I had envisioned were interrupted by an encounter with a Hungarian man en route to Budapest. This encounter could have been a coincidence. Many would say it was that. Others, such as psychoanalysts, would say there is no such thing as a coincidence. Even a few especially attuned Jungian analysts would say it was synchronicity. A Jungian might aver, "What happened between you and this man is more. This is destiny."

I was up early in Catania, Sicily to catch a flight to Rome, from where I would travel east to Budapest. Three friends had presented a panel, "Facing Intimacy: Traversing the Freud-Ferenczi Fault Line," at the Art and Psyche Conference in Siracusa. All of us shared an interest in psychoanalytic history and were drawn to the 1910 Palermo incident between Freud and Ferenczi. I found it hard to part from all the richness and laughter we had together, especially to leave behind the velvet touch of Mediterranean water in our early swims, where we analyzed our dreams as the sun rose each morning.

In Rome, the Hungarian Wizz Airlines announced the gate only twenty minutes before the flight. The aircraft was bright pink. I had intended to study further and write about the Budapest café culture at the turn of the century and the early days of psychoanalysis. There never seemed to be enough time to complete the writing, but then, as I began to learn, each interruption led me in another direction, adding richness and providing me with a sense that time could expand. I had set up several meetings with Hungarians who knew and cared about psychoanalysis and literature, leaving me only a week alone, unfettered by anything.

I boarded the plane, approached my seat, and saw immediately that I had walked into a tense situation. A couple was strongly alienated. The woman was pushed up against the window while the man sat on the aisle. Their exhaustion was palpable. "I think I have the window seat," I said, then, uncharacteristically, "Let me just take the middle." I sat and then wondered why I had. The woman shrank more toward the window in intense relief. The man wasn't as obvious, but it seemed like he had won a struggle, had dominated in the end. Then he turned slightly toward me, and I to him. Turning toward and turning away are profound beginnings and endings all at once. I turned toward this Hungarian man in my haze of fatigue. There was something about him, his heart, an implicit knowing, that caused a mysterious aperture in me. He began to converse in good English. Exhausted as I was, I responded to his benign queries.

Some things in our conversation stood out: surprising matches, intrigues, and subtle coincidences. He was returning from a conference in Perugia with a group of professors, colleagues. The woman by the window was not his wife, not even his girlfriend. I saw and felt his full-body, agonized groan about my stated assumption. He had, though, been convinced to help her out on several matters over the last week. Among those were English translations of her presentations along with economic ideas and sharing a room. "Really! What got you to that?" I asked. Already, I was having uninhibited pleasure in casting out scolding judgments. He invited it. He explained that this was just the way he was. Did he mean a mensch, a gentleman, or a fool?

More conventionally, at some point, he asked me what brought me to Budapest. I described my writing and research on Ferenczi and his friendships among the literati and asked if he knew of this psychoanalyst. He simply said, "Of course," brushing me off. I knew it was not a silly question to ask and began to look at him rather than gaze through him. I told him that I was a psychoanalyst myself. This fact made him sit up, erect, and look at me. I felt another physical response from his body, something else opening up. I didn't feel it was a response to me physically but to something I'd said. I was pretty sure that as a tired traveler, I wore the harried visage of "mama standing at the oven with the food wildly on fire." It's one of my favorite photographs, from the inner cover of The Sopranos' Family Cookbook. *A woman who doesn't care how she looks, in the moment, is free.*

He began to tell me how, not why, he had begun analysis. The "why" he would reveal later. He had a few intriguing secrets. He was being careful not to be overheard by other passengers. He was seeing "Edith," his psychoanalyst, in her home office. He told me, how he would stay for two hours. After their first meeting, as he stood up to say goodbye, she said, "I have something to ask you, and I never do this with patients. I want to hug you. It is because I feel like I've known you before some-where; somewhere in time." He gauged my reaction, and I was there, reassuring him I knew and understood with few words and recognition. I asked how analysts/psychotherapists practice in Budapest. In their homes, he said. He was served tea when he came to his sessions. On his iPhone, we looked at photographs of Edith's green and pastel china tea set. I liked it immensely and said so. He took pleasure in antiques. Fine, small details were important to him, he told me, as he gently removed a blonde hair from my black jacket, saying quietly, "Just let me."

Approaching Budapest, I was moved to say that I felt he might con-sider becoming a psychoanalyst. I softened this by adding that some day, when he was older with more life experience, this could be. He grew excited and said I was the third person who had suggested this. One was his analyst. This made him shake his head in disbelief, and we laughed, but I impressed upon him my seriousness.

My first question when I sat down had been, "About how much is a taxi from the airport to City Centre?" Later, he would arrange everything and accompany me with Uber, which was illegal and difficult in Hungary, as so many things he would explain to me turned out to be. At the baggage claim, he cordially said his good byes to his colleagues and an older professor, whom he loved. My bags arrived and he politely, firmly took over.

By this time, I had started to take in how he looked—both his physicality and his gaze. I was familiar with the trickery of objet petit a, *"Lacan's gaze." What I thought and desired was subjective. I had struggled with differences in desire and suffered over the last year in an intimate relationship, so I was cautious. I did not know what I desired then, regarding him. I was so tired and all I truly wanted was the New York Café in the Hotel Boscolo, wonderful sheets and sleep, and the enticement of tracing "ghosts" who frequented the cafes of 1910.*

Still at baggage, after his goodbyes to colleagues, he walked toward me, and I noticed his dark black hair and beard for the first time. I realized that after two hours of talking on a plane, I couldn't have described him. I could recall the words spoken and the body language. I felt the need to hang onto something he had said as we descended into Budapest, but even then I couldn't remember his exact words, or what preceded it, because I was so tired. He looked at me and said with such feeling, "You are like a finger of God... maybe, in my life." His intensity made me want to capture the meaning before it vanished. I was determined not to forget it. I reflected upon Kosztolányi's statement in Skylark: *"When people go away they vanish, turn to nothing, stop being."[99] They live only in memories, haunting the imagination.*

From baggage claim walking to an Uber, we laughed.

"You know, Dr. Seidler, Tibor, I usually don't make such a conversation with strangers."

"I don't believe it... You are such an outgoing person. You do this all the time. I know it. "

I qualified this: *"Well, I love to travel alone and do talk to strangers but not like this. Nothing comes of it except passing the time."*

He said, laughing, that no, he still didn't believe me, wasn't buying my protest. I remarked that we would have to figure out which of us was lying. This attitude, already?

And then I noticed that a long, slow smile began between us.

Stepping off the plane, I was unaware of what was in motion internally. I was quite relaxed with him. I acquired a sense of security that seemed faintly familiar. This was a different and distant place. I pondered whether it was the place or the man accompanying me that evoked the feeling of living in two centuries, a duality Jung felt was a universal feeling experienced by people. I was filled with longings, unable to articulate the unformed, unfinished thoughts and feelings. The emotions were so strong, making me feel vulnerable. I was there safely, had landed, and, thankfully, didn't have to think but only be guided by him. I was also in a trance state that I didn't fight but enjoyed. It was a familiar state for me, very alluring and relaxing. I expanded into it. I enjoyed the ride.

Together we were driven into Budapest. At a stop light, I listened to his narrative about the outer and then inner regions of Budapest.

"And here is the building, the clinic where my mother worked. Both my parents are physicians. My father a medical professor of several specialties. My mother, a pediatrician, worked with the gypsies. I remember my brother and me waiting outside in the car with my father. He was impatient. She would be late. We would just sit there and watch for her to come out. I would watch the gypsies, the poor people, leaving her clinic. In the car, my father asked her, exasperated, 'Why do you need to see these people?' she would say to him, 'Darling, did I ask you?' She

would get in the car directly from the clinic and, we were then rushing to the Opera. She would just put her lipstick on and be ready. I used to watch her put her lipstick on in the car as my father sped to the Opera House. We would go to our seats. We had the same seats. This is how I grew up."

In front of the clinic, I absentmindedly put my lipstick on. I felt his gaze. It made an intense physical impression, like a finger print on the skin, as if something was being transferred to my body. It caused a sensation, imprinted inside for the aftermath. There were many things to reflect on: his "Finger of God" comments and what older memory might he have of his grandmother or mother when I put my lipstick on. What was evoked between us from the transfer of forgotten experience? Weaving threads of attachment from his body to my body. Memory and longing. The child-like capacity for intimacy with another and the hope for an open and desiring response—but on whose behalf? His or mine? Sitting at a red light in the Uber, I, without thought or memory, had reached for my lipstick. Without care, applied it. Had he told the story before, during or after this small gesture; I could not reconstruct it, but I did know the moment it became written on my body. He embodied "the interruption," where my passionate curiosity was aroused as never before.

On the day of our arrival, September 6, 2015, 3,000 Syrian refugees left the train station in Hungary and walked toward refuge in Vienna.

With thousands of people now massed on the EU's border, and with fall rains and colder weather approaching, the closures threatened to create a new humanitarian crisis

89

of their own. The UN accused Hungary of violating the basic protections set out in the 1951 Refugee convention. Hungary, meanwhile, which sealed its border with Serbia, was firing tear gas, water cannons, and pepper spray at refugees, and arresting those who made it across. Huddled at the train station in Budapest, September 7, over 100,000 began a walk to Vienna.[100]

The terrible flight from the killing in Syria to Hungary. It has been an historic problem in Europe. Borders closed. Europe is at war in 2015. For months, hundreds of men, women and children have marched into Europe, fleeing war, poverty, and hunger. Europe has never known how to deal with migrants. Greece pushed them to Macedonia. Hungary put up a fence. Austria and Germany welcomed them for a time but there was no coordinated strategy for the European Union.

Individual lives and loves are lost in the surges of fleeing migrants. What happens to individual love stories in the midst of war and now the nebulous and shape-shifting war on terrorism? We have novels to tell us the love stories scattered during war. The feeling of connections made and lost amidst larger forces at play was palpable in the atmosphere.

Before breakfast, I walked to the Keleti train station. Why, I didn't know. It was still littered with detritus. Some attempt had been made to remove the trash or sweep it into piles. It was oddly quiet and empty. I wandered around and then returned to the New York Café, musing about migration.

Seated, privileged, in the elegant and opulent New York Café, I was served breakfast in the "deep water," a large room below the main dining level. One could look below and observe us diners seated or standing in the deep water room. In 1894, in the Café beside the women's and gam-

bling rooms, in the deep water was a billiard room. After World War I, a warm food kitchen was established and the deep water was replaced by a restaurant and the New York Café. The New York was once renowned as the most beautiful café in the world. Today, it remains almost in its original splendor. The Café's majestic, Italian Renaissance and Baroque style radiated the literary history and also contrasted with the current economic and political condition in Hungary.

My mind was engaged with the metaphor of deep waters, meaning the depth of connections between regulars' table friends and extended to the connections among four psychoanalysts Freud, Jung, Ferenczi, and Groddeck, who shared a passionate seriousness about the unconscious. Their interwoven connections, particularly their fascination with the unconscious mind, intuition, and thought-transference inspired me. My closest psychoanalytic friends were intrigued not only by the intellect but also by the emotional response of soul and the mysteriousness of the unconscious. We searched and responded to experiential clues in historic correspondences, the deep waters of the unconscious among these historic figures active in their personal experiences of each other. These thoughts lead to musing about what I had named "The 3 Septembers," a grouping of historic and recent events, and the deep waters running in time between these dates, in terms of linkages in psychoanalytic history:

September 1910: Freud and Ferenczi in Sicily, the Palermo incident

September 2012: The beginning of silent writing: a contemporary emulation of Sándor Ferenczi's and Ignotus's experiments in thought transference.

September 2015: Art and Psyche: Layers and Liminality conference, Siracusa, Sicily. Three friends conduct a free-write

experiment and present "Facing Intimacy: Traversing the Lega-
cy of Palermo in History, Writing, Friendship and the Analytic
Encounter."

I was processing all of this at the time of my second meeting with Dr.
Tibor Seidler.

I rode down the elevator and saw him at reception. Then he saw me, as
if I was familiar but very different. He laughed and said, "What hap-
pened to you? You are now rested?!" I wondered, did I look that different?
Apparently. He had wondered whether I would show up, then said, "Did
you think I would show up?" He had considered what it might feel like
to be in my position and said, "I like to get into people's minds." I had
considered him not showing up but was 90% sure that he would. I told
him, "I would have been disappointed if you did not come." This made
him smile, deeply.

With a sense of complicity, we walked out of the grand entrance of
the Hotel Boscolo and the day began. Tibor had a plan. I let it unfold.
He was in charge of my welfare. I reached for his arm. With this gesture
everything changed forever between us.

He divulged one of his secrets that morning while sitting in his car.

"My parents are really my grandparents. When I was three and my
brother was two, my mother was unable to care for me and abandoned
us. At that time, my father was already gone. There was never any ques-
tion about our welfare or who would be my mother. Still, the haunting
of my abandonment has been in my life, part of my personality."

We sat in a neighborhood restaurant wrapped in lavender blankets
on the porch chairs. He said, "I want you to enjoy champagne; I will

not drink. It can be a problem here, just one drink while driving can cause big trouble here."

We drove up in the hills in Buda, near Tibor's home where he walked his dog each morning when he was not traveling. The view of the Buda Castle. His view. We walked around the village-like castle grounds, ran into tourists and gypsies playing string instruments. He remarked that he used to play these as a child. "My mother made me take lessons." I gathered he had a lot of exposure to the arts, facilitated by his mother, or actually, his grandmother. My mother had done the same for me. I thought about it as we drifted into the entrance of the Franz Liszt Museum.

As we walked, I went over this in my mind: A chance meeting on the flight from Rome to Budapest. The tension between the presumed couple. His and her relief when I sat in between. "How much is a taxi from the airport to the Boscolo?" The natural and immediate turn toward him and away from the other. Even in those tiny seconds, the attraction began. Turning toward and remaining there in the grip of it. The conversation was graceful, unpressured, and deep. Later, I would move to hold his arm, to rest on his arm for hours as we walked and talked. I initiated, without awareness. He accepted this. We merged. When I took my arm away later, he would say, "No, you use me, like this, put your arm here on mine." There is a word for that feeling: familiar. There was also a feeling of timelessness.

That audacity, his glance and something exotic behind it. He was drawn to me, and I took notice. The lighting, panorama, the kaleidoscope of old buildings, graffiti, narrow winding streets, fashion, gentrification, poverty, all pulsed. Pest was a traffic jam. I was tired from walking, spaced out. I had thoughts of being overcome with the disease of love, of generations past, channeling literati, dead poets who lingered. Aged stone, deep colors of painted wooden frames, and the wrought iron gated alcoves, rusted copper. Crystalline lighting, texture spread out from narrowness. Gaps of sun and blue sky today, a shimmering. My mind wandered, and if this only took a few seconds, it was compatible with him. He held my arm for hours, and I his, as we walked, talked, dissociated, with the sense of oldness around. He proclaimed out of nowhere, "Age doesn't matter!" as he faced me he released my arm and said it again. How out of context, I thought, as I had not been paying attention to him per se but to the whole experience: the rhythm of his walking and those quickly paced rockets of projection taking me away from modern Buda and Pest. Chasing those ghosts. He was protective of me in the best way. I gauged his manner of serious depth which he could instantly abandon. For me, this capacity marked a rare quality. Somewhat ruefully, I began to recognize that he was like me.

I was in the Central Café looking at a blown-up photograph of the poet Ady. He appealed to me. His style, his deep dark eyes, his élan. I traveled back in time among the dark wood panels and carved pillars. Upstairs, the headquarters of the journal Nyugat. For his son-in-law, Bertalan Frankl, Károly Seeman transformed the building into a coffeehouse. This place, I read, became a center for the spirit of the capital and thrived during this time. I knew that I was visually taking in a remodel recreating the essence of the café during the literati gathering. The birth of Nyugat took place here, in a café, and would be read in a café.

Where were the women? They met here on Wednesdays, whereas the writers of Nyugat met here every Tuesday. Frequent members were Ady, Babits, Kosztolányi, Karinthy, Oszkár Gellért (of the Gellért baths), and Aladás Schöpflin. The café, its former glorious days gone by, seemed peaceful but infused with energy. Kosztolányi's photo looked remarkably like Oscar Wilde. Deep reddish-brown leather booths and chairs, marble-topped tables, light fixtures well placed and subtle. Perfect lighting tempered to the outdoor light changes.

Down a small street in the Jewish quarter, I thought about language in various ways, and how lacking Americans are in their assumptions and dependence upon English language dominating communication. Tibor spoke Hungarian, English, German, Spanish, and French. I could comprehend and get by with Spanish. I thought about having to procure those hard-to-find English translations of Hungarian novelists and poets. I mused about how Freud was considered by some to be a literary master. Freud wrote eloquently and was widely recognized among those familiar with German literature. Thomas Mann, Hermann Hesse, and Albert Einstein praised him as a stylist whose writing yielded master-pieces.[101] Another of my associations was the importance of language with regard to desire. Freud used words that were steeped in classic mythology: for example, Eros, *for the erotic, and* Psyche, *for the soul. Devoid of such classical context these words not only lose much of their meaning but may be invested with opposing meanings.[102] As I tried to understand that Eros was imbued with Beauty, and Psyche symbolized the expression of the soul's longing, I noticed my free associations at that moment surprised me and my desires felt impossible. It occurred to me that only a 63-year-old psychoanalyst would be thinking those thoughts while walking arm in arm with a 36-year-old man. I was aware of my unexpected adventure with Tibor and, occurring simultaneously, my pursuit of Hungarian intellectuals on the fringe of society.*

I saw an aqua sign that read "Massolit" hung on some wooden doors, inside a second set of wrought iron doors that were open. I noticed graffiti on the stone wall above high, oval-arched doors. I wanted to find English translations of Hungarian authors. Opening a chain-link door, which I associated with Karinthy, a writer and one of Ferenczi's regulars, opening the door felt reminiscent of Karinthy's 1929 article, "Chain-Links," and his concept of six degrees of separation. On a wooden table, I discovered an English translation of Márai's book of verses, The

Withering World. *I began to read. The printed words moved toward me as if seeking me from the past. Marái's sentiments enchanted me, and I then realized that souls have no chronological age.*

Thirty-Six

What can come next? Solitude and a dream,
A deeper, darker dream than in the sad
Prime of life – you're further down the stream
What's left is solitude and flesh unclad.
No life for you, no wall standing to claim.
Pictures in frames: no pictures and no frames
Nothing to mourn. And nobody to mourn it.
The wind, washing a corpse, snarling to scorn it.[103]

Sixty-Three

It forfeits Reason and the virgin-clean
Intellect, and the chivalrous flash of swords
In noble words: good faith's no longer keen
To spill its blood, freedom, to burst its cords.
Instead, it mutters. Stands back. Ancestry,
Faith and the old world, view, it can ignore.
It brags about the Jewish pharmacy
It "requisitioned" without paying for.[104]

I revisited my conversation with Tibor on the plane:
    "What brings you to Budapest?"
    "Well, many things, I'm researching the psychoanalyst Sándor Fer-enczi, have you heard of him?"

"Of course."

"What do you do?"

"I'm a psychoanalyst."

At my response, he stopped cold and began to smile. It was easy for him. I could feel him become more interested. There was a palpable sense of something exotic and unstoppable occurring already.

Pictures of his golden retriever on his iPhone. His love and fondness for the dog, which was boarded due to his travels to Perugia. Then he would go to Madrid and Granada. He would leave Budapest the same day as I. We had five days in the same city.

He pointedly did not want to be overheard.

Stories of his childhood. Stories of his activities deriving from his sense of social justice. Other stories he didn't tell.

The "Finger of God" comment, his smile, wondering why we had come into each other's lives as he held his head, shaking it in disbelief in his hands.

As we walked near the Parliament, he interrupted my thoughts with a pronouncement: "It is so sad. Hungary is now the East." His concern for my welfare had been interrupted by our close proximity to the walls of "East" Russian carvings near the Parliament buildings. This glance wounded him. His pain over being near them disoriented him. He grew angry.

"Russia, the Russian rule, it's as if it has never left. I hate to leave Budapest, I love it here but it is not the same. It is unbearable. I'll probably go to live in Berlin." Then, irritably, "Where do you want to go?"

I said, "Anywhere but here."

Tibor had a sense of social justice and helped writers speak to "the people against the fascism" in an underground newspaper and social media. He was ashamed of his government, as stance he spoke of casually,

*as though it were a given. He had an air about him, and I perceived an
attitude of tolerance.*

*I felt all of this as we walked. Our compatible worldview may have
been built explicitly through our varied intellectual backgrounds that
had in common a sense of people's suffering. We'd developed a mentality
that yielded an attitude of tolerance. I had a growing awareness of implicit knowledge between us. We shared a deeper level of meaning from
which all later forms of meaning emerge. This connection was hard to
pin down, but it was the kind that comes into play the minute someone
walks into the room. We were in it.*

*We had tea at a book café in Lotz Hall, Andrassy Ut. We sat in
leather chairs. He ordered something special with tea. Tibor was dis-
satisfied with the cake but tolerated and dismissed this detail. I drifted
off, melting into this Café of Ladies' Romantic Dreams. Hanging from
the high ceiling, chandeliers lit gilt-framed paintings mounted in the
ceiling, beveled glass in octagon patterns formed the oval windows, and
the marble-topped tables were surrounded with leather chairs. Sounds of
conversations amidst coffee recalled a distant time of beauty. I thought
about a scene described by Kosztolányi in* Nyugat:

> The bells were ringing for noon when they reached the
> Grand Boulevard. Budapest, the youthful city, was in full
> splendor. It was early September and the sun gold plated
> the facades of the houses. They let their heads be bathed in
> the bright sunshine. The sky was blue, inexhaustibly blue,
> like the ceiling of newly painted apartments that were
> sticky and smelled of paint. Literally everything was new
> around them.[105]

I must have a photograph of him! Tibor didn't like to be photographed, a preference that I shared. Feeling ephemeral about time and transience, I said, "Don't look. Ignore me and read the papers." Both of us were tyrants. I successfully captured him. I then read him the two poems from Márai's The Withering World *that I felt applied to us at ages 36 and age 63.*

He liked the verse referring to "age 63" and Márai's concept of the intellectual virgin.[106] He laughed at it but couldn't relate to "age 36," yet I could. I was glad to have our ages out, fully aware that he was open to hearing this difference, but possibly it was not relevant. I needed only to mention the poems and plant the seeds in his psyche, because I was already attuned to my secret worry about "vanishing." In his introduction to his book of verses, Márai wrote, "People disappeared, as if I were dreaming; Houses flew off and away on featherweight wings. I stared at the ground. I saw footprints they'd pressed. That's how I lived in bombed out Budapest."[107]

At the flower shop, Tibor's sweet florist friend was so warm, so pleased to see him. She began practicing her art. I was completely distracted by my internal reverie. They conversed in Hungarian. He casually asked me what kind of flowers I liked.

"Roses and dahlias."

"She, my friend, the florist, doesn't like dahlias." They laughed conspiratorially, and I felt clueless. He handed me a beautiful bouquet made for me in plain sight. The gifts. The details. The perception and intuition about me. I loved it all. The experience was so unexpected.

The sweetness of his gestures through the day, the wine and the flowers, were tinged with undercurrents of erotic transference. They suggested possibilities with an awareness of promise. What was the promise that a new way of seeing and discovery brings?

Literally, all of this felt "new," as Kosztolányi wrote in his poems and novels.[108]

It was dark, the ending of the day, as we sat in his parked car. He, leaning against his window. He crossed his arms, and I could tell he didn't want the time to end. Abruptly, we talked about what was sexual appeal. I mumbled something about the brain and mind and then stopped, killing the conversation. We wanted to push the conversation but could not. The eroticism of language, words spoken, and words held inside. The way he silently looked at me—the way we held each other's gaze. Feeling each other without words.

I could hardly sleep. Desire. We want to live inside the others' desire for us. Experience it. What we want is to feel the other's desire for us. To live inside the other's desire.

Das Unheimlich—*a sense of the uncanny occurring. I thought again of riding together in the Uber, coming close to the clinic where his mother had worked, and how I distractedly put on my lipstick. Looking back, this gesture triggered something old for him. The air between us became different. A pause... silence. Only a few seconds of time where something penetrated, and in the pause, the vein of past lives and connections was opened. I would realize this much later. I don't know explicitly if he ever did. I hoped that there would be occasion to ask.*

As I took out the tube of lipstick on the drive from the airport, something shifted from him to me. I was not registering it yet. His gaze, his warmth, a pause, and a thawing began inside me and, perhaps, between us both, melting the secret parts of each other as he told me the story of his mother transitioning from work to family, connecting autobiographical nuance.

"She would come out from the clinic, get into the car, put on her lipstick..."

I thought about how my experience with Tibor felt uncanny. My encounter with das Unheimlich *gave me pause many times. At first, I recognized that my feelings were familiar, as if I had known them (and him) before but had no conscious thought or memory. Because these feelings made me pause, I held my desire in check. I savored this liminal space with its fine edge of longing. From then on, any gesture between us was tied to deep and unpredictable undercurrents. Neither of us was immune. He had exclaimed randomly yet pointedly, "I have three mink coats for the winters here." He laughed deeply at himself, gauging my reaction. It made an impression and made me laugh but for different reasons. There was no possibility of immunity at all.*

I thought of Márai's passage:

> But there was something in their hearts and their movements, in the eyes of the women and in the glances of the men, that shone. It was as if someone had sent a secret signal to tell them that life was not simply a matter of rules, prohibitions, and chains, but of passions that were less rational, less directed, and freer that they had hitherto believed. And for a moment they understood the signal and smiled at each other.[109]

The shadow corridors were infused with golden light. We moved together. We are all migrating, outside of imagination and consciousness, going toward, caught in liminal space. Led by phantasy, aware of the daydream, we gather the dream from the reverie and travel the pathways from our minds and those at our feet.

I now spend an increasing amount of my time imagining minds, in life and in my writing. It is the aesthetics of embodied feelings which moves me. What I was feeling was not a precise emotion but a surge. I sensed the tragic amassing of ineffable feelings, yet there was a complexity and beauty in the experience. With great patience, I tried to understand these emotions of unbearable quality. Only imagination can protect against a fatal absence of beauty in a soul. I was deeply drawn toward the feelings that emerged, all so transient, and did not want them to vanish. Careful to avoid a rupture of my life just yet, I began to travel in my mind and look to the minds of others.

What had occurred was unexpected. I learned that the sensuality of encounters was not separate from but a part of the learning process. "A day like any other and a day unlike any other"—echoes of imagined words channeled from Ferenczi as he joined his regulars on a day in 1910. My day with Tibor was not separate from my research but a part of it. Our chance encounter expanded possibilities in a manner that could not have been planned. Like Stefan Zweig, the author of Confusion,

> by allowing the interruption, I was cast into confusion by every chance occurrence. A passion of the mind... [is] never assuaged by any final act of devotion. It is always in flux, but can never flow entirely away; like the spirit, it is eternally insatiable. *So when he came close, it was never close enough for me.*[110]

With Tibor, I experienced "I know that you know I know." Every intimacy quivered with possibility. It was confusing to wonder if I was so alone in my subjective experience. I hoped I was not a fool. I desired more with him. I ached as I felt the time pass and the impracticality of keeping such an attachment going. Please don't end. Let it go, it's best to detach. *The worlds' voices told me this. They wanted to ground me in reality. It felt like death. I had heeded my wilder impulses and turned away from my determination to get things done as planned. The passions of the mind and of the body are braided together with unacknowledged desires. Without any conscious working towards a preconceived intention, I took his hand. It marked a turning point in my life.*

I thought about Freud's walk and conversation with a taciturn poet during the summer after the war that had robbed their world of its beauties. A powerful emotional factor was disturbing their judgment. As Freud said, "What spoiled their enjoyment of beauty was . . . a revolt in their minds against mourning. The idea that this beauty was transient gave the sensitive mind a foretaste of mourning over its decrease."[III] Thoughts of beauty's transience interfered with their enjoyment of it.

Not too long after my return from Budapest, I closed my eyes and visualized a time and place when I felt that old and new souls were closely aligned. Voluptuous light hovered distantly, glimmering in my imagination. "Distant years of beauty" is a phrase I heard from a Hungarian friend who was recalling a vivid connection to the world of Central Europe. As my Hungarian friends have said, the Russians attempted to kill their sensitivities and identities, saying there was no such thing as a Central Europe. As Tibor said of Hungary today, "It is, sadly, the East."

A month after my return home, prior to the Charlie Hebdo attacks in Paris, we spoke on WhatsApp about old souls. Tibor said, "I've always been an old soul; that old feeling." When younger, he had talked to his rabbi about having old feelings and was assured that it was normal to carry ancestor's feelings from the Holocaust. The ancestors' pain. I wondered at what age he noticed? There was a nine-hour time difference between us. He seemed open to late hours. He was young and could take it. He was very busy. I worried I might never hear from him again despite a glimpse of shared meaning. With my imagination engaged, I was in deep trouble. Deep waters. The life of the mind, expansive, unbound, the intimacy of shared meanings or at least imagined meaning were a powerful combination of qualities. Mutual experiences imbued with these factors made me caution myself. I needed to pause, keeping my thoughts in the present. I didn't know then, but the emigration trails of the Ferenczi Archives would be revealed early in the next year, uncovering how the paths of friends have crossed.

In Carol Maso's book, Break Every Rule: Essays on Language, Longing, and Moments of Desire, I read, "One has to figure out how to go on after the intensity of the moment—one longs for everything," including "a certain spaciousness, that there would be time and room for it all."[112] Three months later, I had a dream: I am in Italy, Germany, or Hungary. I cannot specifically locate the place but it is summer and light.

Why those three countries? Italy, happy, kicked back. Germany, efficient, a place to land to get to another... but parts are fascinating. Hungary, exotic and deeply passionate—the strongest feeling.

Post-dream, I considered a migratory trail of psychoanalytic history from these parts of Europe, from the correspondences of Freud, Ferenczi, Jung, and Groddeck, to correspondence and literary trusts appearing after Ferenczi's death; Ferenczi's notes and fragments found by Michael Balint, literary executor of Ferenczi's estate; Balint's death in 1970, with those papers kept by Enid Balint until 1981 and then entrusted to Andre Haynal and his team to be delivered to the Archives of the British Psychoanalytical Society. Alive in my dream were all of these links in the chain of history in the emigration of documents carried by trusted friends from Budapest to Bern, Paris, Geneva, and London to form the Ferenczi Archives. I wondered: What will be the pattern and memory of Tibor's and my connection over time in four month's time? Will we vanish? Will we meet again? Will our connection continue to grow through technology, not into a full dimensional relationship but a partial contemporary one nonetheless?

I eagerly anticipated a special gathering of psychoanalysts at The André Haynal Seminar at The New Center in Los Angeles. Haynal, an eminent Hungarian psychoanalyst and Ferenczi scholar, became the guardian of memory for Ferenczi, shepherding the papers of the Ferenczi Archives at the request of Enid Balint (Michael Balint's widow) in 1981. I first met Haynal in 2015 at the 14th International Sándor Ferenczi Conference in Toronto. A panel of three—Haynal and I along with Judit Meszáros, President of the International Sándor Ferenczi Foundation—presented on Ferenczi: "Exile of Analysts, and Migration of Archives." I had written to Haynal about my hope to discuss psychoanalysis and literature. He wrote back excitedly that he wanted to share a story about the novelist Márai. Their families had been close friends, spending vacations together. Whether my connection to each of them was a chance to share a glimpse of personal history was luck or synchronicity, I could hardly wait.

On the day before the Haynal Seminar, something made me pause as I sat at my desk. I was spinning ideas around lightly when it occurred to me that I should send an email message asking Tibor whether he knew Haynal—a single question taking only a few seconds. Like a bolt of lightning, he responded. A coup de foudre. The aperture opened and all questions of chance encounter and coincidence flooded our international digital space.

"I can't believe this! He is my grandfather's oldest and best friend! Yes, my family grew up with him. He and my grandfather were raised together. We love him. I know him and his family so well. You have made me so happy! "

I wished he were there so I could shake him and exclaim, "Don't you realize? I can't believe this didn't come up in your mind!? Tibor, how amazing and fascinating, yes, to me, but then, what were you thinking?"

Psychoanalysts know that there is no such thing as a coincidence. Literary critic Shoshana Felman argues that :

> psychoanalytic knowledge... is itself necessarily a purloined (lost, displaced, or misplaced) letter: it is never simply there, at our disposal to apply. It is something that we necessarily keep losing and have to keep working at to find again. But we cannot find it (have it) once and for all. Like the purloined letter, psychoanalysis always has to be recovered.[113]

Hidden in plain sight, the purloined letter! The necessary loss, the possible recovery, the omission; that purloined letter. Again and more strongly, the "Finger of God" was there between us, our hands extended, almost touching.

Through his family, Tibor has this legacy: the remnants of Old Hungary, the suffering and causalities of the past, the Jewish intellectuals, and the embodiment of dignity giving way to the embodiment of the human. What parts of this legacy and inheritance might be carried by him as he grows older, I wondered? He will sense it, I feel. It is already there within him. What survives to be carried by the other?

I wanted to check myself and the preponderance of details that stay within me: Did I get this all wrong? Was Dr. Tibor Pal Seidler a fiction? Was this experience entirely my imagination? Most days, the world feels resistant to the unconscious, negating the intuitive possibility, but there was something living in the unconscious, and I was having a tremendous animation of it.

I was struggling to articulate what has happened to me and what changed. The emotions were about love, but once written, that word was limited. It helped a little when I read Hungarian author Magda Szabo's The Door, about an unusual relationship between a woman and her housekeeper. She wrote that affection cannot always be expressed in calm, ordinary, articulate ways and that one cannot prescribe the form it should take for anyone else. I was struck by this and thought: Not the love for children, husbands, parents, friends but something new from the past tapped into a place hidden inside. It came without expectation. From that moment on, another kind of emotion, a love crossing known boundaries, a gravely tinged desire began to emerge. Something was uncovered, was aroused, making contact. It was something that another carries (for me).

I then read poet and writer Anne Carson's *Eros the Bittersweet*, which helped me place my experience more clearly. She recounted the speech of Aristophanes, in Plato's Symposium, in which he accounts for the nature of human Eros:

> Human beings were originally round organisms, each com-posed of two people joined together as one perfect sphere. These rolled about everywhere and were exceedingly happy. But the spherical creatures grew overambitious, thinking to roll right up to Olympus, so Zeus chopped each of them in two... "Sliced in two like a flatfish," says Aristophanes, 'each of us is perpetually hunting for the matching half of himself.'... All desire is for a part of oneself gone missing.[114]

My experience began to unscramble something deep within me, and as it began to turn on me, it acquired a vividness forever colored by the events in Budapest. We have a mysterious rela-tionship with our unconscious—that part of ourselves that won't settle. I was restless and aware of a battle within myself, preoc-cupied about unconscious phantasy and reverie fantasy. Reverie was more accessible certainly. Maybe I imagined it all, rich fod-der for imaginative writing, veiled mementos of a vanished past? Imagination can be far more rewarding than reality. I made a choice. My attitude would remain open to the possibility of beau-ty (a redemption from shattering). In my individual, small way, I will contribute to the legacy of Ferenczi and his friendships. I cannot do this alone. It will depend upon the mutuality of my friendships.

We are all migrating outside of consciousness.

I want to ask who took seats 11F and 11D on the flight from Rome to Budapest. Why did I take the unassigned middle seat, against my desire, when I rightly could have insisted on the one I had planned and chosen by the window? Turning toward or turning away. We made a choice. Friendships between Freud and Ferenczi; Ferenczi and Ignotus; Ferenczi and the Balints; the Balints and Andre Haynal; Andre and his cherished childhood friend, grandfather of Dr. Tibor Seidler; then Tibor and me. All of us, sitting in those places. How easily I might have turned away but did not. I want to say to Tibor: Yes, you were truly right: Finger of God. What made you say that?

On the phone, I prepared to say goodbye. but Tibor said, "Don't say that. Hungarians never say goodbye. They say, see you again."

How did he know? What was hidden inside of him? How did he sense what was beloved in me? How did our connecting together, by chance, recover aspects of ourselves that were silent? I am not sure whether he consciously knew or even considered this possibility, but it was his intuition that came first. Uncovered, recovered, he found me.

The distant years of beauty are evocative. I am attuned to them and any possibility for their presence today. I was unable to resist pursuing them. I was filled with longing for the beginnings of beauty and the unfinished experience. When I sensed the transition, felt a parting; there was an unspeakable pain and sorrow. It was unfinished because it had only just started and then was slipping away, eluding me, vanishing, as the Hungarian poets and novelists describe it. When I felt myself in the presence of another soul who might understand this mysterious thing, I woke up to live again.

I am certain of three things. Along the way to Budapest, the dialogues of the unconscious began to unfold between Seats 11F and 11D. I have faith that if Tibor were to read this story, a long, slow smile, deep from inside, would begin. There would come a day when I would do anything to be in the sacred space of that intimate friendship where we both felt the other without words.

A year later, I slipped out of the country. I thought I had lost my mind. I arrived in Hungary at night, there was a moon, a bright evening in the fall. Although dark enough and a year past, I recognized him at once. This time I saw with my heart. I was tempted to explain everything, but that wasn't what I wanted to do. It seemed impossible anyway. I'd never lied to him. He'd never promised me anything. Remembering that it was he who first felt the mysterious connection between us seemingly out of nowhere, I made it clear straight away why I'd come.

I needed a refuge. Finger of God.

CHAPTER 9

One Morning in May, 1910, Café Royal, Budapest

Ferenczi looked out of his apartment window at the Hotel Royal across the street. He began his walk to join his friends at their table. He walked slowly, musing:

I didn't sleep much last night, and it doesn't seem to matter or affect my sense of well-being today. I feel so refreshed and such extraordinary satisfaction! I am reassured that future generations can have the prospect of free and open discourse. I, myself, seem to have changed somewhat from recent talks in Vienna with Freud, which has helped me discover, actually, rediscover, something that had eluded me—the individual strivings of the libido. Now here in Budapest, I am, of course, thinking about the day's patients: one who is reading the newspapers to check for the impending danger of Halley's Comet and one who I had to expel a while ago, her state of transference having used the catastrophe threatened by the oncoming comet.[115] Having made that association, I wanted to write to Freud. I put to him and will again put to friends at the café, particularly our circle of sociologists, yesterday's experience of teaching.

I was invited to give a lecture on the new Freudian theories, exploring the unconscious. I cannot fall asleep easily because of this great revolution in psychology, and in fact, I am so aware that there is a revolution in everything connected with psychology, well, I cannot sleep! It is astonishing to me that all of this is happening in my lifetime. These young sociologists were actually the most intelligent and understanding audience that I have ever had the opportunity to address. There were seven or eight young doctoral candidates. Truly, youth is our only hope, I wrote to Freud. They have enthusiasm. I am bringing into the course three non-physicians, an educator (Sándor Varjas), a gifted writer (Ignotus), and the chief director of the National Theater (Sándor Hevesi).[116] Here they are. It inspires me seeing these friends around the table. I see them laughing at something Kosztolányi has said. They are all talking, interrupting. Márai looks intent but somber... I love all of this!

Ferenczi saw Márai, Kosztolányi, Ady, Ignotus, and Karinthy in conversation, all talking at once, excited about the comet. I imagine this scene.

Ferenczi asks, "My friends, who did not sleep well this last night? I did not fear the comet myself and found through a letter from Freud that he has slept soundly himself. Well?"

Kosztolányi replies, "The fear of this comet nearing our earth, even the newspaper illustrations of its tail, have been fascinating, creating hysteria. What might Freud say about this?"

"The comet is like the new psychoanalysis," says Ignotus. "The revolution is coming, and the fear of the unconscious mind, that unknown, creates great threat. Think of this, that our world will not be the same as the comet approaches. It reminds me of another explosion, what we are all experiencing right now, that of the outburst in Hungarian literature and poetry. I feel the publication of Ady's volume in 1906 was the impetus. Will there ever be such "a veritable explosion" as this? The reaction here shows how extraordinarily important literature is to Hungary. We all are in this now, here together in our lifetimes."[117]

Ignotus recites from Ady's "On the Hungarian Fallow": "I walk a land, fertile of old, / but now grown, wild with millet-grass and tares, / this fallow field is Hungary, /for which none cares."[118] *He then comments, "Endre, you are the 'antenna of the Magyar race', a receiver and trans-mitter of certain signals. You are the focus of passions that burn in the mind of the masses."*[119]

Ady replies, "Thank you so very much, my friends. Sometimes it feels like ideas, especially in writing them, take a very long time to reach anyone. But I do, just recently, have a sense that I have been read. I am so gratified."

Karinthy then asks, "If you had heard us arguing about whether the world is actually evolving, in what direction is that occurring, or is the earth just a returning rhythm's game, renewing itself?"

"I have explained that planet earth has never been as tiny, as it is now," says Karinthy, "and this is due to the quickening pulse of physical and verbal communication. Everything returns and renew itself. Today's difference is that the rate of these returns has increased. I have played a game that has grown out of some of our discussions, to find a chain of contacts linking myself with someone anonymous,... and this, in four or five steps, is the six degrees of separation. So something is going on here. Nobody from the group... needs more than five links in the chain to reach, just by using the method of acquaintance, any inhabitant of our Planet."[120]

Ignotus asks Ferenczi, "My friend, tell us of the gathering with the young students and what is planned?" Ferenczi responds, "I intend to lecture them for four weeks, three times a week from nine to eleven p.m. Yesterday, I spoke for two hours without getting tired; you see by this that psychoanalytic teaching is certainly not useless."[121] *He adds, "I realize that Jung was right when he said to gather young men around me whom I can teach and perhaps also love somewhat."*[122]

Márai comments, "This peeling away of the visible world to what is underneath seems to be what Freud and his followers are putting forth. Ferenczi, you've said, as an analyst, not to answer a patient's questions but to turn them back to their sources." Responding, Ferenczi says, "I wrote this to Freud and say it now with you, 'I am firmly convinced that the ideas in Totem will become the nodal point of the study of the history of civilization. I am captivated, astounded and believe that each generation is a link to the other by the idea of transmission by means of unconscious understanding.' Through Freud, my beliefs have been strengthened, that psychoanalysis has shown that everyone possesses in his unconscious mental activity an apparatus that which enables him to interpret other people's reactions, that is, to undo the distortions which other people have imposed on the expression of their feelings.[123] Freud believes that no generation is able to conceal any of its more important mental processes from its successor. This is at the heart of our new world—we possess a structure in our minds, an unconscious understanding, which may have made it possible for other generations to take over their heritage of emotion from our generation—from us."[124]

Afterwards, as Ferenczi walks home, he mulls over the evening's conversation.

How stimulating and satisfying it is to be in the company of curious, open-minded people. They are fascinated with the unconscious mind and intuitively are drawn to its significance. I believe that it is because many of them as thinkers—brilliant thinkers many of them—are inextricably tied to the collective minds of the Magyar masses and have articulated these feelings in literature and poetry. I realize that all of us write in our own various ways. We value reflection, we are inhabited by intense emotions, wildly new ideas—and we write them! For me, psychoanalysis, despite its detractors, remains a complex, nuanced account of interior life that we possess. We all, at this table, read or write poetry. We read *between the lines of novels, or we write them. We read periodicals and journals or write in them, but it is all because we are describing human inner life, and that is what psychoanalysis does as a language, theory, science, or art. All of us at this table today, journalists, poets, novelists, editors, psychoanalysts, are trying to describe the mind and our emotions, our humanness. This reminds me of my thoughts a decade ago when I wrote 'Love in Science': "Doctors and scientists have completely given up the rich source of psychological science, and without hesitation, have left this impassioned material to writers."*[125]

From the future, I converse with him.

"Are we not living in a world at a time similar to those sitting around the regulars' table in Budapest in the early 1900s—we who live in a world transformed by the internet—a world unimaginable to us a mere score of years ago? We witness again the way in which everything returns and renews itself. Though the computer age is beyond their imaginations, their openness to new ideas in science and in art is inspiring. I am respectful of this quality these men possess and share. They cannot imagine how the changes will continue, and yet, I feel they would face this new world with the same boldness and curiosity as they show now in their passionate conversation."

There is a heritage of emotion, the contemporary research and writing about Sándor Ferenczi, from dedicated scholars and colleagues all drawn to him out of a common respect for his intellectual openness, ability to live with uncertainty, his early object relatedness, and his full creative power borne out of an interdisciplinary receptivity and his poet's soul. As a contemporary psychoanalyst, Ferenczi also provided a missing link for the psychoanalytic community's view on human experience and his unorthodox way of treating those who suffer from mental illnesses born of life in the real world.[126]

Ferenczi was truly vibrant in his element. Stimulated by his friends, his presence created a semipermeable membrane, freeing and shaping their minds, just as his was shaped by theirs through his listening deeply. He was teacher and student at once. He was serious but craved *joie de vivre*.

Márai possessed a dark seriousness. He had a brooding, passionate intensity. He was partially present, then drifted off into the beauty of a new thought.

Kosztolányi was elegant and poised for conversation. He wanted to shock his friends with a provocative remark, though knowing he could not because most expected and even needed this from him.

Powerfully handsome, Ady's dark eyes penetrated. He exuded vitality. He also wanted to be seen as a lonely, misunderstood revolutionary. He enjoyed immensely all of the impressions he inspired.

Karinthy offered his humor today. He strongly desired to get his point across, to be understood. He had a sense of irony but also was sensitive to others reactions.

Ignotus carried himself with nobility. He was comfortable with the ideas of others. Sophisticated and courageous, his strength of character was embodied in his demeanor.

I visually encased this tableau in amber. I encoded this meeting in my memory to bear the anxiety of forgetting and the consequences of it vanishing. As if this memory could actually vanish, I departed Budapest.

I imagine, on a Sunday afternoon, Ferenczi and Ignotus sitting side by side with a table between them. Blank pages of white paper. Two pens. Two glasses of water. A carafe of wine. They faced the window on Erzsébet-körút. The light was fading. With a glance, they reached and grasped the other's hand in silence. Ferenczi began to write:

> *The intensity and comfort between us is possible because of your willingness to follow my path without hesitation. You comprehend in the blink of an eye the depths of this new approach. I rely on your keen sense of sniffing out the truth and your disciplined mind, Ignotus. I am transferring something which has been knotted up inside of me. Freud could not or would not understand. You have known me since my early days, and now, meeting at The Royal Café, you are my sounding board. I feel such gratitude for your leadership in embracing the new ideas of psychoanalysis. I think of all the writing you have courageously published: new ideas about dreams, several of Freud's pieces translated into Hungarian, and all the various articles by Kosztolányi, Karinthy, Hollós, Ady, and Jozef. You were always receptive to the new ideas of psychoanalysis, and you were willing to try an analysis with me. It seems that you were most taken with the unconscious dialogue between two people and also that of the analysis itself as a creative endeavor between two persons. Perhaps, with these ideas from our discussion of my paper, "Introjection and Transference," you have understood the libidinal forces at play between doctor and patient? Without this there is no analysis. At the heart of what I find the most important is the relationship between the two individuals and, then, the action taken.*

But now, in this moment, it is my gratitude I'm trying to trans-mit to your mind. I'm struck by the notion that when I think of thought transference, I still find that what I have studied and observed on my visit with psychics is inexplicable. I wrote Freud about this feeling: "When I try to explain what I saw and heard I must admit that I am incapable of doing so."[127] *I digress. I am transferring this thought and all of my true emotions attached to it, gratefully.*

On his scrap of paper, Ignotus wrote,

I am faced with a blank page. I want to put something on it about you, and I also want to transfer a thought to you. Both of us begin with blank pages. I'll start with a simple idea. This is the word I will transfer now: "blank."[128]

Ferenczi waited, receiving, then wrote,

I am a blank. I am trying to remain open to Ignotus's psychic possibility. Can I sense the response, or is it just that we know each other so well? We can read each other's minds. What is stirring within me in our silence is my visit to Frau Seidler, the soothsayer. My thoughts are traveling. Do you see them, know them, or do you travel with me on this wandering trail with mutual thoughts—together traveling the mind?

Ignotus waited to receive from Ferenczi, then wrote his response:

I am thinking of early on when I began my analysis with you. I did not like this commitment and felt compromised as if by a pose, though in the interests of this new science. I and you, too, at the time, felt relief because you, Sándor, couldn't resist paying attention to what was behind whatever it was that either of us was saying. I, on the other hand, paid much attention to the words. I felt as if I was posing as a patient, disingenuous. I had to fight against the desire to talk as friends. This reminds me of our talks about an unconscious dialogue, that there could be in the unconscious of two people, a complete understanding of themselves and the other, without the slightest sense of this in either of their conscious minds. This conception of voices, conscious and unconscious, between two people opens up so many possibilities in human relationships. For us, we will have to be satisfied with our willingness to experiment in the trust of each other. My true request was very conscious, I collaborated with the analysis because I was your very curious, trusting friend. Our trial analysis broke down and our friendship strengthened. I, in our friendship, was to be the "book you had not finished reading".[129]

Once the analysis had ended, as good friends, we could deal with the tensions between us, those of authority and equality and of intellect and emotion, by oscillating this tension. I learned the difficult way, by experiment, in trying to be your patient, that the doctor–patient relationship of psychoanalysis was too hard for me as your friend. There are many questions remaining and stimulated for us about why a psychoanalytic relationship is different from a friendship. In our enthusiasm, we seem to be willing to explore many ways of knowing each other.

At this moment, I am most interested in what the possibilities are for thought transference. I am wondering what the differences are between two open-minded, close friends who know each other's histories and a true psychic, such as Frau Seidler. When Frau

Seidler has a successful experiment with someone whom she does not know, it must be something different from our more ordinary and known intimacy. You wrote to Freud that "she can do things heretofore thought impossible."[130] *I want to see how far we can go in the transfer of thoughts. Now, when I think about what you have said about Freud's idea, another kind of transfer, that of psychoanalytic transference and countertransference feelings, I ask whether these feelings are real? In other words, if there is a feeling of love between this pair, does this mean these feelings are ordinary or unreal? And just what kind of love, after all? All of these questions about psychic reality and psychic experiment seem related. There seems to be a difference suggested by Freud, but I am not so sure. I am intrigued beyond measure and wonder this very minute what you are picking up? I'll wait a few minutes, and then you must write on your blank page what came up for you.*

Ignotus, my dear friend, you seem so intent. I can feel your mind at work as we sit here this quiet Sunday. While I'm not sure of a simple thought or image that I've received, I thought I felt something from you. What I came to pay attention to first was something I learned from Frau Seidler, and it is worth mentioning. She never knows whether she should interpret an idea—an image that appears to her—in a concrete or abstract sense. She explained that her images were visual. Her comment makes me think that there is also an uncertainty about concrete or symbolic meaning in the interpretation of dreams between psychoanalysts. No visual image comes to me even though I search for it in silence.[131] *Here is what came to me, and it is an emotion about our friendship: I feel an appreciation and recognition from you that I struggle with in other relationships, Freud and Jung, to begin with.*

With them, I am filled with impulses of jealousy, not enough appreciation, and my longing for recognition. I have the thought that these infantile feelings could be with me my entire life. Here in your presence, just for a moment, I feel your understanding. If there was to be any image at all, I could describe it as an opening. You, Ignotus, provide that opening. I see light.

We have been up all night and the darkness is fading. I am tired. Ignotus's hand slips out of mine. I look at our hands, the hands of two men, and notice that something is changing. Surely, we shared the sense that as the sun rises these Monday mornings, we are part of a new and exciting world. We opened our minds and greeted this new world of thinking together. Maybe my mind is playing with me, but on Ignotus's hands, my hands—writing, giving, receiving, and waiting—the skin seems to be peeling away. His hands begin to fade, shape shifting as the dawning light begins, and a feminine hand is in its place.

A woman's hand is writing, writing something on a blank paper. It is very quiet. She seems finished and passes it across the table to a man, who is also silent. It is late afternoon, in a garden, in a different country, in a different time. In a new world. A blend of intensity and serenity, compelling and intriguing. Each friend trying to understand the other, they talk in other contexts, but what will come of the silences and transference of their silent thoughts to the other on these blank pages? He worries that it is tactless to weigh her down with repetitive, unresolvable, purely personal matters; although he has tried to work them out himself. She wants understanding and forgiveness from him, lightening her unsatisfied need for support. She wants to be seen, under-stood. He wants to be met. She cannot be present unless seen. Neither needs to be right about any of it. Perhaps here is the bridge between two friends who need each other differently.

Epilogue

Five years have passed since I read the remarkable paragraph by Ignotus, eulogizing Ferenczi and describing their thought transference experiments. I think about this time span, a century ago and the last five years. What has been transferred? When the world stops, barriers melt away, and what's left is a chain of memory, linking the borderlands between the vanished past, the jagged present, and a hopeful future. That haunting question, "What do we want from each other?" remains. What we need is time and a willingness to resist ephemerality.

Some times in life have such moments of clarity, piercing everything else. It is with this keenness that I think about those moments between and among the regulars, these enduring friends.

Chains that link. The love between friends. Resist ephemerality.

I drive along the foothill road, catching the ocean's reflected light. Something inside of me gently peels away, like the surface of a painting, revealing something hidden beneath that has the power to change me. I feel transparent. I thaw. I feel the change.

I am returning to the regulars' table. There is nowhere else I want to be. I am almost there.

Historical Figures in Ferenczi's World

Endre Ady (1877-1919) was a Hungarian poet whose *New Poems*, published in 1906, produced a literary explosion in Hungary. Its impact was a testimony to the extraordinary importance of literature and poetry in Hungary at the time. *New Poems* has been regarded as a touchstone of modern Hungarian poetry. Ady was a historical and a political and literary phenomenon. He was closely associated with the artistically progressive *Nyugat*, which he also edited in 1912. His fourth collection, *Blood and Gold*, brought him success and critical acclaim. He was interested in politics and became a member of the radical group, Huszadik Szazad (Twentieth Century). In 1908, in Nagyvarad, he was one of the founders of a literary circle, A Holnap (Tomorrow). The circle published an anthology of poems by Ady and others including Mihály Babits, Gyula Juhász, and Béla Balázs.

Mihály Babits (1883-1941), a Hungarian poet, writer, and translator, is best known for his lyric poetry. He was an essayist and translator. He was a staff writer for the *Nyugat* and became an editor-in-chief of the journal in 1929, sharing the role with Zsigmond

Móricz until 1933, a position he held until his death. Influenced by Freudian psychology, he wrote *The Nightmare*, a science fiction novel about a split personality. His poem, *Two Sisters*, is about Desire and Sorrow.

Michael Balint (1896-1970), Hungarian psychoanalyst. Balint spent most of his adult life in England. He was a proponent of the object relations school of psychology. He completed his medical studies in Budapest and began attending the lectures of Sándor Ferenczi, who, in 1919, became the world's first university professor of psychoanalysis. In 1919, at age 21, Balint became interested in psychoanalysis when he met the psychoanalyst Imre Hermann. Balint and his wife, Alice Kovács, began a training analysis with Sándor Ferenczi. He studied with István Hollós and Géza Róheim. In the 1920s, he assumed a leading role in Hungarian psychoanalysis. Balint became Ferenczi's disciple and literary executor. When Ferenczi died in 1933, Balint became administrator of his estate and his successor as director of the Budapest Polyclinic.

Róbert Berény (1887-1953), a Hungarian painter, was one of the avant-garde group known as "The Eight" who introduced cubism and expressionism to Hungarian art. Berény was forced into exile because of his participation in revolutionary movements. Together with Olga Szekely-Kovács, he drew caricatures of the participants at the Eighth Psychoanalytic Congress (1924) in Salzburg.

Sándor Brody (1863-1924) was a Hungarian author and journalist. Beginning in 1882, he was a prolific contributor of articles, stories, novels to the leading literary publications of Hungary, and from 1890 on, wrote for the newspaper *Magyar Hirlap*. He depicted the dark side of life and was a disciple of the modern French realistic school.

Géza Csáth (1887-1919), cousin to Dezső Kosztolányi, was a Hungarian writer, playwright, musician, music critic, and psychiatrist, whom some considered to be a psychopath. He became addicted to morphine in 1910, and most of his dark stories were written during this period. He often descried violent acts in the first person, with powerful insight into the perpetrators' disturbed minds. His collected short stories were published under the title, *Tales Which End Unhappy*.

Georg Groddeck (1866-1934) was a German physician and writer regarded as a pioneer of psychosomatic medicine. He practiced in Baden Baden and, as a pathfinder of psychosomatic medicine, astonished numerous readers and listeners. His book, *The Book of the It* (1923), was widely influential with physicians and psychoanalysts, including Sigmund Freud.

André E. Haynal (1930-), psychoanalyst (IPA), physician, philosopher and author of more than a dozen books and hundreds of other publications, was a leading editor of the Freud/Ferenczi correspondence (1992-2000), and a recipient of the Sigourney Award for his life's work.

István Hollós (1852-1957) was a friend and comrade of Sándor Ferenczi. In 1913, he became vice-president of the Hungarian Psychoanalytic Association. He began his analysis with Ferenczi, then continued with Paul Federn. After World War I, he was in analysis with Freud. Together with Ferenczi, Hollós studied paralytic dementia. After Ferenczi's death, he became president of the Hungarian Psychoanalytic Association.

Attila József (1905-1937) was one of the greatest Hungarian poets of the 20th Century. A poet of great seriousness, he spent his entire life in extreme poverty and suffered from depression. Although his poems are melancholic, they also express József's faith in life's beauty and harmony.

Carl Gustav Jung (1875-1961) was a Swiss psychiatrist and psychotherapist who founded analytical psychology. His work has been influential not only in psychiatry but also in philosophy, archeology, literature, and religious studies. A prolific writer, most of his writings were published after his death. Jung considered individuation to be the central process of human development. He created some of the best known psychological concepts, including archetypes, the collective unconscious, the psychological complex, and extroversion and introversion. Jung corresponded frequently with Sigmund Freud and Sándor Ferenczi.

Frigyes Karinthy (1887-1938), a Hungarian writer, poet, playwright, journalist, satirist, and translator, argued that "art cannot exist without science." He was a friend of Kosztolányi and Géza Csáth, who later introduced him to Freud, and was analyzed by Ferenczi. In 1912, Karinthy entered dynamically into popular literature with five publications: *It Is Snowing*, *The Ballad of Dumb Men*, *Fools Encyclopedia*, *Curved Mirror*, and a literary parody, *You Write Like This?* He was first among his peers to criticize feared dictators Mussolini, Hitler, and Stalin. In 1937, his novel, *A Journey Around My Skull*, was published, describing his brain surgery.

Well known for a dry sense of humor, he noted, "In humor I know no jokes." His story, *Chains,* included his concept of six degrees of separation.

Dezső Kosztolányi (1885-1936) was a Hungarian poet, novelist, and critic whose first volume of poetry was published in 1907, when he then joined the *Nyugat* circle led by Ignotus. In 1910, he achieved immediate success with *The Complaints of a Poor Child.* With gentle humor and a penchant for the macabre, Kosztolányi was a sympathetic observer of human frailty. He was dedicated to the principle of art for art's sake. Author of many short stories, his *Anna Ednes* (1926) and *Wonder Maid* (1947), the empathetic tale of a servant girl, show he was chiefly concerned with artistic form and took little interest in the social questions that absorbed most of the *Nyugat* circle. He was analyzed by his friend Sándor Ferenczi, whose alter ego, Dr. Movister, appears in one of Kosztolányi's most famous novels.

Gyula Krúdy (1878-1933), Hungarian writer and journalist and a friend of Sándor Ferenczi, was an habitué of the cafes and taverns of Budapest. He wrote a series of mesmerizing, revelatory novels that are masterpieces of modern literature. In his novels, he created a world entirely of his own imagination—dreamy, comic, erotic, passionate, and hopeless. The formative ideas of his novels *Sunflower, The Adventures of Sinbad,* and *Life Is a Dream* he discussed with Ferenczi at the Royal Café into the late hours of night. He produced a prolific body of 60 novels and 3000 short stories before dying in relative obscurity on May 12, 1933, ten days before his friend Ferenczi's death.

Sándor Márai (1900-1989), Hungarian novelist and journalist, authored 46 books, mostly novels. He was one of the most influential representatives of middle class literature. His novels explore facets of love; nostalgia for the bygone multiethnic, multicultural society of Austro-Hungarian Empire; and the bond of male friendship. His works include *Embers*, on male friendship; *The Rebels; Casanova in Bolzano*, on romantic love; and *Portrait of a Marriage*, on the relationship between love and class and love and security. He is considered a genius of humanity.

Géza Szilágyi (1875-1958) was a Hungarian novelist, poet, journalist, theatrical producer, and member of the Hungarian Psychoanalytic Society.

Hugó Veigelsberg, or **"Ignotus"** (Latin for "unknown") (1869-1949), was a writer, poet, critic, editor, and organizer. He wrote under the pseudonyms "Dixi," "Pato," "Pal," "Mrs. Emma," and "Tar Lorincz." He was one of the first adherents and supporters of Freudian psychoanalysis in Hungary. In 1913, when the Hungarian Psychoanalytic Association was founded, he was the only non-medical member. Writing under his pen name, Ignotus, his poems, stories and sociological works were distinguished for their lyric individuality. He was a founder of the literary magazine *Nyugat* in 1908, along with Miksa Fenyó and Reno Usuat. He was considered the most influential literary critic of his time. As a literary leader, he was a proponent of the autonomy of literature, of art for art's sake, independent of politics. He was one of Sándor Ferenczi's longest and closest friends.

Excerpt from Ignotus's "Eulogy" for Ferenczi

(As cited in J. Meszaros, 2000, *In Memoriam Ferenczi Sándor*, pp. 37-46; T. Keve, 2012, *Ferenczi and His World*, p. 5)

Many years later, I can see the two of us sat in his consulting room one Sunday afternoon, when he didn't have patients. We sat side by side, in silence, holding hands with our eyes closed, observing our thoughts, and then each scribbling down on a piece of paper what they had thought, what had come to mind, and, comparing the two scraps we saw that what had come into my mind was associated, by the logic of Freudian dream interpretation, with what Ferenczi had thought of,... and so I believed in the transfer of thoughts. And so what was going on, in a small way, in the Városmajor and on Erzsébet Avenue, must have been going on throughout the world on a far grander scale—and today, as the new physics has engendered a new view of the world, the new analysis has engendered a new view of the person.

"Ignotus, the Understanding," by Sándor Ferenczi

(Article published in *Nyugat*, *23* (1924), translated by Andrea Hagymasi, M.A., in collaboration with Christina Griffin, Ph.D., for The Regulars' Table Project.)

To be honest, it was with malicious joy that I welcomed the news that you, dear Hugó, had also joined the ranks of those in whose honor a celebratory issue was published. I went through this myself a good year ago, so I know very well those mixed feelings that emerge in a person at a time like this, especially in the kind of person who, like you and me, does not really believe in ephemerality (at least based on his deepest and most subjective conviction). Albeit a lot of those things that used to surround us at the time of our old friendship have long been gone. Where is the green lawn I was laying on, listening to your always quick-witted, deeply insightful judgments and predictions about everything and everybody, in exchange for which I could offer no more than a few results of my youthful enthusiasm for research? Where are those times, those happy and uneventful years of the pre-war era of Franz Joseph, during which a poem, a felicitous word, or the

spark of a scientific thought could have a sensational and mesmerizing impact in the lives of serious adults?

I do not wish to continue in this tone since we want to cele-
brate, don't we? I will not, therefore, continue the comparison;
rather, I will try to recall what the main thing was that I could
thank you for in the course of my personal development. I can
summarize my impression in one word: it was understanding that
I received from you. It was no small deal, considering that I was
completely alone in the country, representing the most recent
approach in the science of the psyche, against a condescendingly
disdainful or loudly derisive, sometimes cursing crowd. It was a
big thing indeed that, at a time like that, one could come across
a person who was able to comprehend in the blink of an eye the
depths into which the new approach opened a path for further
study, a person who was "only" a poet and a Hungarian writer,
but still followed me on my path without hesitation, relying on
his keen sense of sniffing and disciplined mind. This path was his
path as well since both of us were looking for the Truth. Besides
all these, you were also compelled to have an enormous amount
of ethical courage to incessantly break a lance for me, the lone
fighter, even in front of the public.

All this provided me with ethical help and courage, but I can
thank you for even more than this. For me, you became the forum
whose opinion I could accept as decisive, with almost blind certainty, and you became the "refined reagent" with which I could
test the value of my ideas after I became convinced that what
you liked could not be completely bad and what you frowned
upon must have had some defect. Thus, you and Róbert Berény,
a young painter friend of ours, were like a genuine institution
for me, making my exclusion from societies of the University and

the Academy of Sciences, together with other scientific societies, easily bearable.

Of course, you probably do not know that once you did hurt my feelings when you very thoroughly criticized my written work from the point of view of style. I admit that then I felt discouraged and started to write in a rather dry and objective manner, abandoning all regard to beauty, under the influence [of this criticism] for which I have received rebuke from the readers in return. In conclusion, I have to thank you for this as well, because through your remarks I managed to get one step closer to being free from vanity, without which, I believe, no genuine science can be done.

Many years have passed since we had our last argument; both of us have graying hair, but I at least still cannot believe in ephemerality and often believe that the time will come when there will be no events and we will be able to lay on the lawn again together, immersed in weaving new thoughts.

"Budapest, September 10, 1909," by Dezső Kosztolányi

(Short story published in Nyugat, 1, 1929, translated by Andrea Hagymasi, M.A., in collaboration with Christina Griffin, Ph.D., for The Regulars' Table Project.)

At eleven o'clock in the morning, Esti[1] was still deeply asleep on the couch on which his landlords made his bed.

Somebody reached out to touch him. This made him open his eyes.

From the world, which he had lost in his dream, he first noticed a stern figure sitting on the edge of his couch.

"Did I wake you up?"

"Oh, no."

"I have written a poem," said Sárkány,[2] looking like an excited messenger who arrived from a different planet. "Will you listen to it?"

---

1   Kornél Esti (literal translation: Cornelius Nightly) is the main character in Kosztolányi's cycle of short stories, an expression of his split personality. For more info see http://www.literarycharacters.eu/HU-kornelesti

2   Sárkány: last name meaning 'Dragon'

Without waiting for a response, he started reading it, at a fast pace:

"The moon, this faint lady in the air
Is kissing the wild, negro[3] night,
Drinking champagne..."

"Beautiful," mumbled Esti.

Sárkány was disturbed by the remark. He acted as if he had been interrupted while kissing a woman. He cast an annoyed glance at Esti. However, after he understood the meaning of the word, a grateful smile lit up on his face.

Esti asked his friend, "Start over!"

Sárkány resumed reciting his poem:

"The moon, this faint and airy lady
Is kissing the wild, negro night,
Drinking champagne while her tousled and gloomy hair
Is flowing down on him..."

In his left hand he was holding a piece of squared paper torn from a notebook, pressing his right hand against his face, as if he had a mild toothache. He was reading in that posture.

This boy looked like an unhappy gypsy lead violinist. He was dark and flaming with passion.

His pale face was enwreathed by sooty hair. His mouth was red, almost bloody. There was a copper ring glittering on his hairy index finger.

---

3   At the time, the word 'negro' had no negative connotation in Hungarian.

He was wearing a thin tie. A low-cut, purple vest. Worn but ironed black clothing. Brand new patent leather shoes. He used orchid perfume. This filled the whole room with a penetrating scent.

Esti was listening to the poem with his eyes closed.

Yesterday they were walking together, arm in arm, staring at the moon above the rental apartment blocks and railway warehouses of Ferencváros[4]. Now the same moon emerged behind Esti's closed eyelids, on his darkened eyeballs, just like on yesterday night's firmament. The moon was floating there, the moon of the poem, which, according to the fashion trends of the 1900s, was wearing strong makeup, looking slightly frivolous and pampered. Nevertheless, it appeared to be much more beautiful than in real life.

"Wonderful," exclaimed Esti and jumped up from the couch when the poem ended. "Wonderful!"

"Really?"

"Really."

"Is it better than the 'Crazy Swings'?"

"Not even comparable."

"Will you swear?"

"I swear."

Sárkány was still trembling in the rhythm of his poem. He felt that a very significant event had happened.

Esti was feeling the same. He looked around the month-long untidiness of his rented room. While he was searching for his stockings on the floor, he asked:

"When did you write it?"

---

4   Francistown, a district of Budapest

"Last night. As soon as I got home."

They stayed silent for a while.

Sárkány turned towards him:

"Didn't you write a poem?"

"No," uttered Esti worriedly. "Not yesterday. Where will you submit it?"

"To Független Hirlap."[5]

He sat down at Esti's desk to finalize his poem in ink.

In the meantime Esti was getting dressed with hesitation. He pulled on his pants and planted his feet in front of the washbowl, appearing totally helpless. He pushed his hands into the water and waited. He slightly wet his face. For him, washing up consisted of nothing more at the time. He insisted on preserving his personality so much that he was reluctant to wash off the layers that had settled on him during the day. He considered those who indulged in the superstition of excessive grooming untalented people.

He used neither brush, nor comb. With his fingers he ruffled up his hair, in which feathers from his pillow were stuck, to make it look tousled in a manner that was different from last night's. He was managing his locks in front of the mirror until he caught sight of the head therein that he once imagined for himself and preferred to claim as his own. Then he tied his necktie, with the utmost care.

Sárkány, who was done with copying, was humming a cabaret tune.

"Hush," said Esti, pointing with his head at the door that was blocked with a wardrobe.

---

5   'Independent Daily'

Behind that door lived the owners of the place, two elderly women who were his landladies: enemies of tenants and literature.

Both Esti and Sárkány got sad. They were staring at the wardrobe and saw reality therein, which always made them feel helpless.

"What shall we do?" they asked, whispering.

There was a day ahead of them, a new day, with its limitless freedom and opportunities.

In any case, they walked downstairs and sat down in the restaurant of a nearby hotel.

Here they were still on their own.

The restaurant was gleaming white. The purple light of arc lamps was rustling above the freshly washed cambric tablecloths – these untouched, virgin altars at which nobody had taken communion yet. Waiters were hustling and bustling before work, with dazzling shirt-fronts, freshly, like gallant escorts in the ballroom. An escalator rattled between the walls of the hotel. Through the half-open door there was a view of the foyer, the leather armchairs, and the palms. A chambermaid kept yawning there, with the divine promise of accidental love. They were taking delight in this morning's still life. They imagined that then, when there was nobody else there but them, everything was theirs, and because they imagined it, everything was theirs indeed.

Neither of them was hungry but they decided to have lunch, just to get it over with. On the pretext that he would by all means sell his new poem to the publisher as early as at three but no later than between six and seven o'clock, Sárkány asked for a loan of two koronas[6], giving his word of honor. They had rolled anchovy

---

6   Hungarian korona (crown), divided into 100 fillérs, was the currency at the time.

fillet, dunking fresh bread rolls into the oil until it was gone, leg of venison with cranberry, and vanilla cream. They drank hosszúlépés[7]. They smoked a green-spotted, light Media each.

The bells were ringing for noon when they reached the Grand Boulevard. Budapest, the youthful city, was in full splendor. It was early September and the sun gold plated the façades of the houses. They let their heads be bathed in the bright sunshine. The sky was blue, inexhaustibly blue, like the ceiling of newly-painted apartments that were still sticky and smelled of paint. Literally everything was new around them. The school year had just started at the time. Elementary school students waddled with bags on their backs, clutching the stickers that they had received from the stationer as gifts.

Esti and Sárkány stopped at the same time.

A young man was approaching them, walking backwards, crawling like a crab, at a very fast pace, which was indicative of exceptional experience.

A straw hat from a bazaar was dancing on the crown of his head. He was wearing white porcelain pants, with a grey, thick felt overcoat and a flesh-tinted caoutchouc wristband. He was swinging an iron stick.

In the following moment, they also turned around and started walking with their backs towards him, in a hasty manner.

When they eventually faced him, they burst out laughing.

"Servus, you bastard," they roared at him and hugged each other.

---

7 Hungarian spritzer made of 1 deciliter wine (red or white) and 2 deciliters of soda water.

At last they were together, the three of them, Kanicky, Sárkány and Esti. Nobody was missing, the chain locked up, the world became complete: their society – the Balkan Society – got together, whose primary tasks included the free, brave, and public exercise of such and similar operations.

The pedestrians were watching these three cheerful guys, these three flighty, immature fellows disapprovingly, with slight contempt and concealed interest. They did not understand them and thus hated them for it.

Kanicky spat on the asphalt. His saliva was black. It was as black as ink.

He was chewing on black liquorice.

They found liquorice in his left pocket, and medlar in the right one, in a paper bag.

They were heading towards their headquarters, the coffeehouse.

On the way, Sárkány was reading his new poem aloud to Kanicky as well. In the display window of a furniture store there stood a bedroom, with two wide poplar wood beds, both made up, with silk comforters, pillows, and bedside tables. In their thoughts they laid in the bed, with their shoes on. They pictured an ideal spouse in front of them, of the size of a titanic porcelain doll, with a beehive hairdo and eyebrows lined in ink. All this seemed so distant and improbable that they felt ashamed of their daydreaming and set it aside as a poetic theme. They walked into a pet shop. They were bargaining over a monkey, asking how much a lion might cost. The merchant, seeing what kind of customers he was facing, made them leave the shop.

"Maybe we should greet people," suggested Kanicky.

Hence they greeted everybody who was walking towards them. The three hats were raised at the same time, as if touched by a

magic wand. They were looking honestly into the eyes of the greeted. Sometimes those individuals were happy that they were held
in such high esteem, sometimes, however, they were surprised,
noticed the mischievous prank and, after giving the friends the
once-over, they walked on. All in all, the statistics were pretty
good that day. From fifteen "persons" eleven returned the salute.

Then they stopped doing this as well.

Esti bought two balloons at the corner of Rákóczi Road. He
tied the strings to his button hole and picked up his pace to reach
his friends whom he had lost.

Not far from the coffeehouse a gathering started to form. They
said that two gentlemen were quarreling, one pushed the other
and they were about to slap each other.

An agitated exchange of words could be heard:

"I won't tolerate such remarks!"

"You are impertinent and insolent!"

"You are impertinent! You are insolent!"

Kanicky and Sárkány faintly looked eye to eye. Kanicky was
raising his hand. A calm gentlemen intervened:

"But gentlemen, for Heaven's sake, gentlemen!"

Kanicky cast a glance at the calm gentlemen and, as he always
did on such occasions, asked Sárkány:

"Will you tell me, please, who this is?"

"I don't know."

"Come with me, then."

He took Sárkány's arm, as if nothing had happened and, at the
amazement of the bystanders, wandered off hugging one another.
Esti joined them.

"Did they fall for it?" he asked.

"Yes, they did," they responded, cackling.

They released one of the balloons.

That was how they arrived at the coffeehouse.

The coffeehouse – during lunch break – was quiet and deserted. Cleaning women were moving up and down, with brooms and pails, wiping the marble tables. Belated morning coffee drinkers were paying their bills. A scrawny acrobat was passing along the ladies' salon.

They were roasting the afternoon coffee. Its aroma was tickling their noses. The gallery above, with its twisted and gilded Baroque columns, like a Buddhist temple, seemed to be waiting for something.

They sat down here, at their regular table. First they strived to settle their financial issues. Kanicky had sixteen fillérs, Sárkány had thirty, and Esti had one korona and four fillérs. It was not sufficient for fighting that day's battle.

Sárkány, who had the best prospects for the day because he had written a poem, beckoned to the morning head waiter, made him count down twenty Princeszász[8] cigars, ordered coffee, then after presenting his manuscript that he might sell to Fületlen[9] at three in the afternoon but no later than between six and seven o'clock, asked him for a loan of ten koronas. The head waiter placed the sum in front of him with resignation. Esti ordered a double espresso. Kanicky asked for sodium bicarbonate, water, and a slip of paper.

He took the soda bicarbonate. Slowly, out of pure absent-mindedness, he supped the three glasses of water in front of him, even though Esti tapped his cigarette ash into one of them. He start-

---

8 It is probably the Hungarian slang pronunciation and spelling for **Princesa cigar.**

9 Nickname for Független Hirlap. (Literal meaning for 'fületlen': earless.)

ed writing a croquis[10] to make money. He suddenly jumped up, clutching his head. He had to make an urgent phone call. Nervous troubles were swarming around his shiny forehead. He asked his friends to escort him to the telephone booth. He did not like being alone.

On the way down to the ground floor, they were jostling each other, cracking jokes, running into acquaintances, and forgot about what they actually wanted. There were loathsome figures hanging like leaches to the phones, speaking German, old bastards, forty, forty-five years old, who would kick the bucket soon anyway. Kanicky received a connection half an hour later. He stepped out of the booth triumphantly. The woman would come, at three in the afternoon. He loaned five koronas from Sárkány, giving his word of honor, and thus Esti also got one korona back from the two koronas he had lent a short while ago.

After their financial issues had somehow been resolved, they sat back to their table with relief. Kanicky wrote a few sentences of the croquis. Then he stopped writing again. He summoned a porter and sent a letter to the one whom he had telephoned. They were smoking cigarettes and kept sighing. They were laughing and grieving, in rapid succession. They were waving through the plate-glass window at the women passing by in the street. When the waiter carried fruit in front of them, they gave first names to the different kinds of fruit. The apple became Károly[11], the grapes Ilona[12], the plum Ödön[13], definitely, and the pear, due to its soft-

---

10 Sketch, light essay

11 Charles

12 Helen(a)

13 Hungarian male name, rather rare nowadays

ness and voluptuousness, Jolán,[14] etc. They were itching with some kind of restlessness. They played parlor games with letters, colors, and sounds, mixing and patching everything. They raised the most peculiar questions about what would be if something had not been the way it was. No, they were not satisfied with Creation.

At three Sárkány galloped off to pick up his voucher. The coffeehouse was buzzing, the noise in the gallery was getting stronger. In this harsh racket they were feeling the rhythm of their lives and that they were headed somewhere, moving forward. Every table, every booth was occupied. Storm clouds were towering from the smoke. It felt good to stretch out in this steamy, warm puddle, thinking about nothing, just watching how it boiled and bubbled, knowing that those who were splish-splashing in it would slowly be slackened, steamed, cooked, concocted together into one single bowl of buzzing broth. They could see their everyday acquaintances, scattered around at different tables, on velvet sofas and chairs. They all had arrived.

Here was Bogár, the young novelist. Playing the piano, here was Arácsy, the painter, who had gotten himself photographed in a Florentine knight's armour with a dagger on his side. Here was Beleznay, the famous art collector, a personal acquaintance of Wilde and Rodin. Here was Szilvás, the "marquis" with an ivory-handled walking stick, an incomparable conversationalist who blended our newest slang words in a humourous and masterful manner with the obsolete expressions used in lexicons on neologisms, archeologists' papers, and inaugural academic speeches. Here was Elián, the neurologist, Gólya, the applied artist, Sóti, the scientist who studied the origins of our folk tales, Boldog,

---

14 Hungarian female name

the modern photographer who conducted his studies in Berlin, and Kopunovits, the apprentice actor in the tragedy genre. Here was Dayka, the blonde son of a big landowner who immersed himself in Neo-Kantianism and talked about epistemology. Here was Kovács who never talked but collected stamps and smiled sarcastically. Here was Mokosay who had already visited Paris, read Verlaine and Baudelaire in the French original and quoted from the French original, with great enthusiasm and bad pronunciation. Here was Belényes, the "sworn chemist" who lost his job because of committing some kind of irregularity and now loitered around editorial offices of newspapers and provided data for investigative reporters. Here was Kotra, the dramaturg who demanded pure literature, the purest possible literature, on the stage as well, and wanted to stage the drama entitled "Waiting for Death", which was being written by Géza, his friend sitting next to him, and in which there were no humans, only objects, and the key and the keyhole were engaged in a long and deep metaphysical argument with one another. Here was Rex, the art dealer who, defying public opinion, praised Rippl-Rónai and lashed out at Benczúr[15]. Here was Ikrinszky, the astronomer, Christian, the conferencier, Magass, the composer. Here was Pirnik, the international Social Democrat. Here was Scartabelli, the aesthetician and polyhistor, who in his warm bass voice discussed partly Wundt and experimental psychology, partly the small streets of Buda, in a highly sentimental manner, emphasizing that he was not sentimental. Here was Eyssen, about whom no one knew more than the fact that he had syphilis. Here was Bolta, who did

---

15 József Rippl-Rónai (1861-1927) was a Hungarian Impressionist painter, Gyula Benczúr (1844-1920) was a Hungarian historical painter.

not consider Petőfi a poet because Jenő Komjáthy was the poet[16]. Here was Spitzer, who thought that Max Nordau was the greatest mind in the world. Here was Wesselényi, a highbrow assistant pharmacist. Here was Sebes, who had already two short stories published in daily papers and one that had been accepted. Here was Moldvai, the lyricist. Here was Czakó, another lyricist. Here was Erdődy-Erlauer, a third lyricist. Here was Valér V. Vándory, the literary translator who translated from every language but spoke none, including his mother tongue. Here was Specht, the child of rich parents, a modest and shy young man who had not written anything but he had been treated in a lunatic asylum for two years and constantly carried in his pocket a stamped certificate signed by three psychiatrists that he was totally sane. All in all, everybody was here.

These people talked all at once. About whether or not man had free will, what shape the plague bacterium was, what the wages were in England, how far Sirius was, what Nietzsche meant by "eternal recurrence", whether or not homosexuality was justifiable and whether Anatole France was Jewish. They wanted to penetrate into the meaning of everything, quickly and thoroughly because, although they were all very young, slightly older than twenty, they felt as if they did not have much time left.

Esti only vaguely knew this company. He was not always sure about who was who, but it was not a problem; the persons concerned were still not sure who they were, either, since their personality and character was in the making right then and right there. On one occasion he mixed a photographer with a poet, on

---

16 Sándor Petőfi (1823-1849) is one of the most famous and talented poets in Hungarian literature, who died young in the War of Independence from the Austrian Empire. Jenő Komjáthy (1858-1859) is a lesser known and appreciated Hungarian poet.

another occasion he was mistaken for a photographer. Neither of them took offence. They told each other their life stories, memories, previous love affairs, plans, and then, if they saw fit, they also introduced themselves, out of formality, and might have even memorized one another's names.

He was sitting among them, listening to the droning of their words. He was attracted to them. Amidst this chaos, each voice hit a key in his soul, he was a relative of everybody and everything. He did not understand life. He had no clue why he had been born into this world. In his way of thinking, everybody who received a share of this adventure of unknown purpose, which ended in annihilation, was exempt from any responsibility and was entitled to do what he or she wanted, for example, lie down along the main road and start wailing without any reason, without deserving any special reprimand. Nevertheless, just because he considered life pointless in its entirety, he understood each small individual part thereof, each person without exception, each noble and evil point of view, and each theory, and he did make them all his own right away. If somebody had talked to him sensibly for five minutes to make him convert to the Muslim faith, he would have converted to it, provided that they spared him from the burden of having to act, took him by his word and did not give him any time to still backtrack later.

In his opinion, living like this, amidst smaller manifestations of senselessness within a greater senselessness, was not so foolish, moreover, it was perhaps the most correct, most stylish way of life. Besides, he did need this wild disorder, this penetrating marinade. He wanted to write. He was looking forward to the moment when his desperation and disgust would culminate in an urge to retch, and then everything would get ripped out of him, everything that was important and essential, not only what was secondary and incidental. But this moment had not arrived yet. He did not feel bad enough to write. He kept devouring nicotine and ordered a new cup of double espresso to pat his heart and further torture his perpetually curious, eager and playful spirit, while he feverishly watched his own internal pulsation and read his own heart rate, which was one hundred and thirty beats. He counted these beats as happily as a usurer would count his money.

He was surrounded with women, like the "lady from Csongrád," who took fortnightly trips to Budapest and spent her free time among writers, leaving her husband in the countryside. There were literary girls, fake demons, a pale lady acrobat who must have been sick, and a yellow-faced, puffy woman, huge and horrible like Klytaimnestra. They were sitting around there, wearing white, blue, and black, blooming in the hot swamp like the water-lilies in Hévíz.[17] He yearned for all of them. His irresolute eyes were zigzagging restlessly among them. He enjoyed the machinations and deadly dangers of chance, which might change his life and turn into destiny in any second. He was watching the hands of the "lady from Csongrád," the nails at the end of her soft fingers that she had polished pink and clipped into a pointed shape. He imagined that this woman could possibly be his destiny, but he was horrified of her strange nails, which could scratch tenderly like rose thorns, and rejected the thought in alarm. The "lady from Csongrád" asked what he was thinking. Esti broke into a supercilious smile, lied something in a way to make sure that the woman could still think what he was thinking.

---

17 Hévíz is a popular spa in Hungary with the world's second-largest thermal lake.

Kanicky bent his head onto his friend's chest. He was not waiting for every woman, only the one who, due to some misunderstanding, did not show up, even though three o'clock had passed a long time ago. The porter, whom he had sent away with the important message as early as at noon, did not return, either. He hired another porter to look for the previous porter. He walked over to the coffeehouse on the other side of the street and to the small restaurant called "Rabló."[18] On the way back, he stopped by the phone booth and made phone calls to several places for an hour, to no avail. He waved at Esti, signaling that everything was all over. He ordered a kis-irodalmi,[19] which he consumed with gusto, then he took some sodium bicarbonate again.

Sárkány, who had been lost since three o'clock, arrived around seven. He radiated happiness. He told them that a completely new period opened up in his life. He met with that alleged kindergarten teacher about whom he had talked so much to his friends that they might have known her even better than he himself. They made it up and now, at long last, everything would be in order for real, for good. Esti and Kanicky heard it daily that a new period had started in Sárkány's life and that he had found the one and only woman. They were more interested in his voucher. Sárkány's face turned dark. First of all, he announced that he had spent all his money. As for the voucher, what happened was that at three, he paid a visit in a due form to the publisher who was in a bad mood, gave him the cold shoulder and snapped at him to come

---

18 Rabló = Robber

19 Kis-irodalmi (tál) = small literary (platter). A dish that was originally designed for the writers and artist who had a small budget but a great taste and an even greater prestige. The writers left their mark; their heritage is called 'kis irodalmi tál' which is a selection of small bites of the actual dishes.

back between six and seven. He did show up between six and seven and handed over his poem gently and politely, begged to get paid for it, which the publisher, this curly-haired and bloody scoundrel who looked like Herod, received with unheard-of insults, spat and trod on his manuscript and literally kicked him out. Based on his individual presentation, his friends had a hard time visualizing how that scene had taken place, but they felt indignant at the tactlessness of the publisher.

So there stood the three of them, stone broke, with a whole load of espressos, cigarettes, porter costs behind them, not to speak of the kis-irodalmi cold cuts, and with an empty and bleak night ahead of them. Something had to be done. Life was rippling indifferently. Scartabelli was talking to them about Bhagavad Gita and Nirvana, in the midst of moderate interest. Valér V. Vándory was translating a French novel. He enquired of the persons who were present about what 'derechef' might mean in Hungarian. Mokosay criticized his pronunciation. He asked for the book. He was of the opinion that it was the name of a flower that was not endemic to our country. Others suspected some kind of obscenity. Most suggested that he should omit that word, so Valér V. Vándory omitted the whole section and resumed his work. Hannibal, the night vendor, stepped in at that moment, offering with a frozen grin on his poker face his naughty picture postcards that showed weird figures when held up against the light. Immediately after this, he presented his condoms, as if the mere sight of the picture postcards would be harmful to our health.

Esti stood up and looked for the head waiter of the night shift. He got ten koronas out of him. He received one gold coin. He was supposed to share it with his friends whom he also owed some money from earlier. After complicated calculations, he even considered the deal somewhat good, hoping that at least he would get back immediately that one korona that Sárkány had not paid him back from that day. But then he decided otherwise. He simply escaped. He was running and running down the street. He planned to go to the Writers' Club and win at least sixty koronas, then divide the amount fraternally, into three parts, twenty koronas to each one of them. At the gaming table, in front of the "coffin," sat Homona, the famous winner, a respectable journalist, who made a living by blackmailing the banks. Esti thought it was a bad omen. Nevertheless, he still threw the round, enticing gold coin on the green betting field, in one sum. His bet was raked in inconspicuously.

He could ascertain this right away. However, he kept standing there, frozen for a good ten minutes, as if he had been waiting for a worldwide cataclysm to change the unappealable decision made by fate.

In the coffeehouse they were waiting for him like a savior. Kanicky was surrounded by the two porters who had returned and demanded their money. He tried for a while to explain to them with rational reasons that they were not right, then he took an aspirin and, guarded by the porters, dashed off his croquis within five minutes. Then, also guarded by the porters, he sold it. He even brought home some money and threw some to his friends.

They walked to Mária Street to see Sárkány who was expecting a letter from the kindergarten teacher. They visited the Kanickys, where they drank some tea. The whole family stayed in one huge room. One of Kanicky's aunts was painting, the other one was playing the piano, and the third one was facing the wall, standing frozen, it was not known why, as long as the guests were there. The father, a kind and loveable elderly gentleman, was sitting in the middle of the room, writing with the poise of old age, dipping his pen rhythmically into the inkwell. He tapped off the surplus ink from the tip of the pen carefully, undisturbed by the raging noise that surrounded him. After the locking of the gate, they left the building. Kanicky was reciting The Tragedy of Man[20] loudly. On a dark square, a peasant with a whip in his hand, who looked like a coachman, walked straight towards him, put his hand on his shoulder and said:

"You know what? I'd rather pay back your fifty fillers, but give the halter back to me."

"No," replied Kanicky, "I need the halter."

Esti did not understand this talk of the fifty fillers and the halter; he did not know whether they conspired against him or it was an accident, so he started to feel afraid. The black rags of the night were lying scattered around him. He would have liked to be at home at last, lie on his couch alone. He hated himself and hated his friends as well, but he could not break away from them. He was gripped by the same fear as in his childhood when he felt that he had committed something wrong. Looking stiff from the day's work, people under the gas lamps stared into his face as if they had been watching him. They were walking behind him with the loud pattering of their shoes, as if they had been following him. He was happy when they entered the "Rabló". That at least was an enclosed place.

The barrel piano was playing the overture to Tannhäuser. His nephew, medical student József Gách held his two palms to Esti's nose and made him smell it. He had done his first dissection that

---

20 Imre Madách: The Tragedy of Man (1861) - a classic dramatic poem, which elaborates on ideas comparable to Goethe's Faust. (Required reading in high school.)

day. Faltay, the sandal-wearing Tolstoyan, had semolina pudding for dinner. Bisszám, the bearded, young theosophist, whose face was as red as an apple and his white teeth were like porcelain, warned them, looking warmly into their eyes, to love Nature and live in harmony with the Universe.

They thought they still had time to do that, so they dropped by the coffeehouse again.

There, the high-brow intellectual revelry had already become depraved. The gallery was occupied by the upcoming generation, eighteen and nineteen-year-old youngsters. Beside espressos with rum and Egyptian cigarettes, Putterl, little Hajnal, and little Wallig established a combative periodical at the highest possible standard, against fossilized traditions, the Academy, and old people. Next to them, Abmentis wrote lyrics to music and sang his first line: "Oh lágy madárkám."[21] Instead of the word "lágy," he would have needed another iambic word with two syllables, consequently he kept trying to say the line like this: "Oh kemény madárkám."[22] It would not have been proper to use, though. While singing, he was looking for a new adjective that would fit the text as well as the little bird. Erdődy-Erlauer represented the older generation. It was the first booth where he was brooding over and staring at his manuscript, on which he wrote the following: "My life is like..." But he had not since been able to resume writing. He did not know what his life was like, he could not find a simile for it, which was no wonder at all: Erdődy-Erlauer's life did not resemble anything, it was exactly like Esti's life itself.

---

21 Oh, my soft little bird!
22 Oh, my hard little bird!

They left them there, with their manuscripts, with their bitter, sorrow-filled lives. They were wandering around the bank of River Danube, around the Eastern Railway Station. They kept picking up the apprentice writers in every part of the city, who were roving about in the dead of the night, as if they had been on duty: Eyssen, Szilvás, the Neo-Kantian Dayka, Moldvai, Czakó, and some others who were also likely to have something to do with the arts and spiritual sciences: music pedagogue Orbán, Csiszér, and Valentini, who was some kind of cabinet-maker. This weather-beaten little group found itself among the houses of Ferencváros around three o'clock in the morning.

There was a prostitute standing at the corner. Eyssen started to talk to her. The others were surrounding them. They would not miss any opportunity to study the depth of life and flaunt their well-informedness in the meantime. They were addressing these women informally, in a patronizing and familiar manner, even though the women were usually much older than them, at least as old as their mother's lady friends whom they had to give a kiss on the hand at home, politely, making a deep bow. This disrespectful licentiousness increased their self-esteem.

They were discussing something. A dialogue was taking place between them and the prostitute, which was interrupted moment after moment by the group's loud guffaw. Eyssen was flourishing his cocky cane in the middle. The woman was responding quietly. What she said could not be heard.

Esti was standing further away from them, alone. He did not want to participate in this game. He found it tasteless and indecent the way it was going. Despite the fact that he knew this neighborhood better than any of them. He knew these streets at every time of the day and the night, because some kind of familiar

horror chased him this way on many occasions by making him
jump out of bed at home and run here. He knew this quarter early
in the morning when nobody would be coming here; on Saturday
nights, at the time of the great to-do between eight and eleven;
in the summer heat on sweltering hot days, at noon, between one
and two, when girls were shining in the sticky heat like cheap silk
candy in their gaudy dresses. He knew each house individually,
the doors and windows in which lamps lit up and went out. He
also knew the men who were loitering here absent-mindedly, as if
they were looking for somebody else, slipping in with their eyes
closed, making sure that at least they did not see anybody else
for the time being. He knew the indifferent as well as the dumb
who were eyeing up chicks openly. He knew the fat and lonely
old gentlemen who smoked their cigars through a cigar-holder,
watched bemusedly the pale spinsters that walked on the other
side of the street and then, deciding out of the blue, took off towards a chocolate-colored gate as if somebody had pulled them
by strings. He knew the technical terms of this urban landscape,
which hit his ears every now and then and were related to the
objective details of the profession.[23] He knew mainly the women,
each one of them, in person or by sight, the kind and the apa-
thetic brute, the aristocratic and the peasantly, the lanky and the
dwarfish, the ones with a pink scar on their chin, or with a bite
mark that looks like a worm. He also knew the ones that led dogs
on leashes, the ones that wore glasses, and the appalling one who
sometimes showed up early in the morning, covering her face
with a double black veil because her nose was missing. And he
did know this girl who was being entertained by his friends; he

---

23 The author probably hints at the [ancient profession of] prostitution.

had seen her several times when he walked this way. He watched her and took account of her.

The girl took Eyssen's cane and they slowly started to make their way to a side street. The group was following them. Esti also quickened his steps to follow them and see what was in the making again. They rang the gatebell and entered, all eleven of them.

There was such growing clamour inside, in the low, ground-floor room, as in a house on fire when the firemen arrive. They were squalling and hollering because of the weirdness of the situation. The woman was afraid that a policeman would take down her name for night-time disturbance and causing scandal. She tried to hush them, to no avail. Five of them sat down on her bed with such vehemence that it gave a cracking sound and almost collapsed under their weight. The marquis extended his arms and, in well-rounded Baroque-style sentences, preached to the woman to emerge from the moral swamp and mend her ways. Then he blessed her like his child and called her "violet". Eyssen was looking at her adhesive photographs. Sárkány rummaged around her belongings. Czakó lifted the lid from the red-glazed pot on the iron stove, in which he found the leftovers of her dinner, frozen beef stew with tarhonya,²⁴ that she had put away for the following day.

The woman stamped her feet to make silence. She kept watching the guys to make sure they would not to carry off anything. Her eyes were quivering, looking from side to side.

Kanicky whispered something to Sárkány. Sárkány whispered it on to the others, the news made its way around and, by the time

---

24 Hungarian browned egg barley

it hit all of the eleven eardrums, an all-encompassing and stormy guffaw burst out. They were all looking at the woman.

It could be seen under the lamp that she was indeed much older than they had thought outside, in the street. She was wearing a round black beauty patch above her chin and a reddish blonde, thick wig. According to Kanicky, under the wig her head was as bald as a billiard ball and she did not have one single tooth left. That was what they were laughing about.

The atmosphere turned sour. No one was saying a word. They regretted already that they had come in and were wondering how they could get out of here. The woman was eyeing them up and down distrustfully. There was worry floating in her eyes, which she was afraid to pronounce.

Then Kanicky sidled to the door and sneaked away, without saying goodbye. He was followed by Sárkány, then Szilvás, then Eyssen, then Moldvai, then Czakó, then Dayka, then Valentini, Csiszér, and Orbán. The last one was Esti.

The gang was escaping in a stampede.

"Are you leaving as well?" the woman looked up in alarm.

"I am," he put his hand on the door handle. "Good night."

"Good night."

Esti opened the door that his friends slammed shut in front of his nose as a joke. He was listening to what was going on outside.

His buddies gathered in the stairwell, waiting for the caretaker. There sounded a frightful scream, Sárkány's voice, then Kanicky's voice, who was yelling something horrible towards the room.

"What is it?" asked the woman.

"Nothing," responded Esti and closed the door not to hear it.

The woman looked at him.

"So have you changed your mind? Are you staying here?"

"Yes, I am," said Esti. "I may sit down for a minute," and he was still standing there.

At this moment the gate closed with a loud thud; the caretaker let them out. Everything turned quiet.

"They are crazy," remarked the woman in the sudden silence.

She shrugged her shoulders, in an awkward manner.

Esti pitied her for this movement. His heart, his sick heart, got filled with tears like a sponge.

After a few moments, however, a loud noise blared again in front of the window. The company was standing under it. Eyssen pulled his cane over the let-down roller blinds, and familiar voices wished Esti a good night, lots of luck, and plenty of fun.

He was looking towards the window like somebody who had been trapped and would like to climb out of the trap. They had left him there. He became the victim of a prank, the victim of the last, nasty prank. The clamour ceased. There was silence again: eternal, big silence.

"They are gone," whispered the woman and locked the door with a key.

Esti wanted to remedy a formal mistake. He could not bear it if somebody was insulted face to face. He found it so painful that he would rather stay with boring people for hours, because he could not find the proper way to tactfully shake them off, and he often had the feeling that he would rather die than tell somebody openly that he or she was not needed in this world. Once he realized that the essence of life was rudeness and that we said bad things about one another behind one another's back anyway, and in our thoughts we constantly wished for each another's destruction and death, he believed that genuine politeness, based on good will and mutual forgiveness, was the greatest human virtue. Despite his own will, this was what he strove to practice everywhere and with everybody. No one can do more on this Earth.

The woman pushed a cane chair towards him. She, too, sat down on the couch, facing him.

They were right: she was not young any more, she looked rather weary, and there was something lunatic in her smile. It was possible, however, to look at her differently. He started to fire up his imagination, so reality vanished. No, they were not right, they were exaggerating: her skin was withered, but white, lily-white. And she has her teeth, almost all of them. He got to like her misty, green cat eyes, her round faded-hungry face, and narrow forehead.

"What's your name?"

"Paula," responded the woman with a soft, stopped-up voice.

Words made a mesmerizing impact on Esti. This name had the impact of a faded tea rose on him. He closed his eyes.

"What were you before?"

"Haircomber."

At this point Esti clutched at her hands and skirt desperately.

At the barracks they sounded reveille. Soldiers were lining up for marching out of the barracks courtyard. The captain was at the front on his dancing horse, holding his unsheathed sword and crunching German words of command between his teeth. As a result, this formidable machinery, which consisted of human flesh and steel, started to move and turned around the corner to Üllői Avenue. Handsome lieutenants, smelling of eau de Cologne, kept giving orders. Their swords and yellow-black tassels reflected the shine of the morning. Emperor [of Austria] and King [of Hungary] Francis Joseph I was the ruler, sitting on his high throne in Vienna.

Esti was walking home along Üllői Avenue. The gate was already open, so he did not even need to pay gate-money.[25] He ran up to the fourth floor, to his room, in which Sárkány woke him up at eleven in the morning the day before.

He found a postcard on his desk, from the countryside, from his parents. That made him thrilled.

The postcard was sent from his uncle's famous birthday party, where the three related families met every year: the Csendes, Esti, and Gách families. The menu included ludaskása,[26] cigánypecsenye[27], and vanilla-almond crescents. Lots and lots of greetings from everybody: from relatives and acquaintances, and even from his sister's girlfriend. His brother wrote that he had a strict head teacher, his sister said that she went to a dance school, and his mother let him know that she would like to see him. He should visit them at the end of the month, for grape harvest, by all means. His father only signed his name with his strict, cursive handwriting.

Esti was touched as he was reading the card several times in a row. In his mind, he was at home at the vineyard, in the arbour overgrown with ampelopsis, among the green velvet armchairs of the salon. He was hugging his dear ones with adoration, because, above all else, he was a good boy and a loving brother. He thought: "my mother has an amethyst bangle which is of the same color as her eyes." He thought: "my father is also up already, he has been working since four o'clock." He thought: "nothing will become of me, I will fall into depravity." He thought: "I will be

---

25 Fee paid to the caretaker of a building for opening the gate during the night.

26 Boiled millet with goose giblets.

27 Fried or spit-roasted pork cutlets.

everything." He thought: "I will die next year, at the age of twenty-one." He thought: "I will never die." He thought all this, all at the same time.

The day he had just experienced was crammed and busy, but it did not really differ from the other days of his life. His confusion had solidified into massive sorrow. He kept tight hold of the postcard, trembling, seeking for protection, hiding behind this rural peace, where his roots and strength were to be found.

Self-accusation gnawed at him. He went through Spanish irregular verbs once. Then he got undressed.

But he got up again. He answered the postcard so that he could mail his letter the following morning, as soon as he would go downstairs.

He wrote the following:

"My dear parents and siblings, thank you for your kind remembrance of me. In my thoughts I am always with you."

He should have responded something to the invitation as well. Then Sárkány and Kanicky came to his mind, whom he did not love less than his siblings.

He continued as follows:

"Unfortunately, I cannot travel home very soon. The new literature is in turmoil. I have to stay here, I need to be on the alert."

He was contemplating a better excuse, but finally this was all he added:

"I am working."

Endnotes

1. Moreau-Ricaud, M. (2012). Healing boredom: Ferenczi and his circle of literary friends. In J. Szekacs-Weisz & T. Keve (Eds.), *Ferenczi and his world: Rekindling the spirit of the Budapest world* (pp. 87-96). London, England: Karnac, pp. 91-92.

2. Ibid., pp. 91-92.

3. Lukács, J. (1988). *Budapest 1900: A historical portrait of a city and its culture.* New York, NY: Grove Press, pp. 150-151.

4. Ibid., p. 151.

5. Moreau-Ricaud, "Healing boredom," pp. 91-92.

6. Keve, T. (2012). Ferenczi remembered. In J. Szekacs-Weisz & T. Keve (Eds.), *Ferenczi and his world: Rekindling the spirit of the Budapest world* (pp. 1-29). London, England: Karnac, p. 10.

7. Lukács, *Budapest 1900*, p. 152.

8. I am using the term "regulars' table" as the English translation of German word *stammtisch*, which means a table in a pub restaurant, or cafe reserved for regular customers.

9. Keve, "Ferenczi remembered," p. 13.

10. Kosztolányi, D. (1993). *Skylark* (R. Aczel, Trans.). New York, NY: New York Review of Books, p. 17. (Original work published 1924)

11. Balint, M. (1988). Notes for a preface by Michael Balint. In S. Ferenczi (1988), *The clinical diary of Sándor Ferenczi* (J. Dupont, Ed.) (M. Balint & N. Z. Jackson, Trans.) (pp. 221-222). Cambridge, MA: Harvard University Press.

12. DuPont, J. (1988). Introduction. In S. Ferenczi, *The clinical diary of Sándor Ferenczi* (J. Dupont, Ed.) (M. Balint & N. Z. Jackson, Trans.) (pp. xi–xxvii). Cambridge, MA: Harvard University Press, xx-xxi. Author's license.
13. Haynal, A., & Haynal, V. (2015). Ferenczi's attitude (S. K. Wang, Trans.). In A. Harris & S. Kuchuck (Eds.), *The legacy of Sándor Ferenczi: From ghost to ancestor* (pp. 52-74). London, England: Routledge.
14. Dupont, "Introduction," p. xxvi.
15. Balint, M. (1968). *The basic fault.* New York, NY: Brunner/Mazel, pp. 149-152.
16. Ibid., pp. 149-156.
17. Ferenczi, S., & Groddeck, G. (2002). *The Sandor Ferenczi-Georg Groddeck correspondence, 1921-1933* (C. Fortune, Ed.) (J. Cohen, E. Petersdorff, & N. Ruebsaat, Trans.). New York, NY: Other Press, pp. 8-9.
18. Keve, "Ferenczi remembered," p. 20.
19. Ibid.
20. Balint, *The basic fault,* p. 151.
21. Ibid, p. 151. Verbatim quote: "I am certain that the feeling of not being understood by Freud hindered him."*Note:* Michael Balint went on to achieve what he set out to do in his work on trauma and regression and carried forward Ferenczi's work. His books, *Primary Love and Psycho-Analytic Technique* (1952) and *The Basic Fault: Therapeutic Aspects of Regression* (1968) reflect a continuation of the Ferenczi tradition of independent thought and the analyst's response to their patients.
22. Krúdy, G. (1998). *The adventures of Sinbad* (G. Szirtes, Trans.). Budapest, Hungary: Central European University Press. (Original work published 1944)
23. Meszaros, J. (2014). *Ferenczi and beyond: Exile of the Budapest School and solidarity in the psychoanalytic movement during the Nazi years* (T. A. Williams, Trans.). London, England: Karnac, p. xxii (Original work published 2008); Balint, M. (2000). Ferenczi Sándor, mint orvos [Sándor Ferenczi as a physician]. In J. Meszaros (Ed.). *In memoriam Ferenczi Sándor* (pp. 148-154). Budapest, Hungary: Muhely. (Original work published 1933), p. 48; Márai, S. (2000). The quick and the dead. In J. Meszaros (Ed.). *In memoriam*

Ferenczi Sándor (pp. 47-50). Budapest, Hungary: Muhely, p. 48. (Original work published 1933)

24. Karinthy, F. (1929). Lancszemek [Chain-links] (Adam Makkai, Trans.). In *Minden maskeppen van* [Everything is otherwise], p. 4. In Karinthy's story, "Chain-Links," which became a play, he presented his concept of "six degrees of separation," now a part of everyday language. Author's license.

25. *Nyugat's* first issue "contained pieces by Ady, Kosztolányi, and Géza Csath—later on the journal would publish writings by Babits, Juhász, Béla Balázs, and Arpad Toth. These writers would later prove to be the defining literary group of the period, and one of the most renowned groups in Hungarian literary history" (Staley, 2009, pp. 34-35).

26. Kosztolanyi, D. (1929). Budapest, 10 September, 1909. *Nyugat, 1*, pp. 21-34. (See Appendix D for English translation by A. Hagymasi, for C. R. Griffin, The Regular's Table Project)

27. Ibid.

28. Hanák, P. (1998). *The garden and the workshop: Essays on the cultural history of Vienna and Budapest*. Princeton, NJ: Princeton University Press, p. xix.

29. Ibid., p. 82.

30. Ibid., pp. 82-91.

31. Mezaros, *Ferenczi and beyond*, pp. 31-32.

32. Ibid., pp. 31-32.

33. Staley, M. (2009). *The first Nyugat generation and the politics of modern literature: Budapest, 1900-1918* [Unpublished thesis]. Central European University, Budapest, Hungary, pp. 38-44.

34. Kosztolányi, D. (1924). *A bús férfi panaszai* [Laments of man of sorrow]. Budapest, Hungary: Franklin.

35. Moreau-Ricaud, "Healing boredom," pp. 92-93.

36. Freud, as cited in Phillips, A. (1994). Secrets. *London Review of Books, 16*(19), pp. 3-5.

37. Freud, S., & Ferenczi, S. (1993). *The correspondence of Sigmund Freud and Sándor Ferenczi, volume 1, 1908-1914* (E. Brabant, E. Falzeder, & P. Giampieri-Deutsch, Eds.) (P. T. Hoffer, Trans.). Cambridge, MA: Harvard University Press. Many examples of Ferenczi's attempts to connect

with Freud are found in their correspondence. Rich with examples are Letter 170 (pp. 217-221) and Letter 171 (pp. 221-223), quoted here.

38. Ferenczi, S. (1988). *The clinical diary of Sándor Ferenczi* (J. Dupont, Ed.) (M. Balint & N. Z. Jackson, Trans.) (pp. 84-85). Cambridge, MA: Harvard University Press.

39. Freud, as cited in Phillips, "Secrets," pp. 3-5.

40. Gluck, M. (2004). The Budapest flaneur: Urban modernity, popular culture, and the "Jewish question" in fin-de-siècle Hungary. *Jewish Social Studies, 10*(3), 1-22.

41. Kirk, J. (2013, October). Bartok's monster: Stalking the dead composer through Transylvania. *Harper's Magazine*, pp. 49-64.

42. Keve, "Ferenczi remembered," pp. 2-3.

43. Kosztolányi, D. (2011). *Kornél Esti* (B. Adams, Trans.) New York, NY: New Directions Books, p. 38. (Original work published in 1933)

44. Ibid., p. 38.

45. Kosztolányi, *Skylark*, p. 15.

46. Márai, S. (2002). *Embers* (C. B. Janeway, Trans). New York, NY: Vintage, 2002, pp. 41-42. (Original work published 1942)

47. Babits, M. (1936). Kosztolányi. *Nyugat, 29*, pp. 395-401.

48. Ferenczi, S. (1924a). Ignotus, a megértő [Ignotus, the understanding]. *Nyugat, 23*. (See Appendix C for English translation by A. Hagymasi for C. R. Griffin, The Regular's Table Project.)

49. Drawing on the works of Baudelaire, C. (1857). *Les fleurs du mal* [The flowers of evil]. Paris, France: Poulet-Malassis. Author's license.

50. de Waal, E. (2010). *The hare with amber eyes: A hidden inheritance.* New York, NY: Picador, p. 72.

51. Freud & Ferenczi, *The correspondence*, Letter 170, pp. 217-220.

52. Ferenczi, S., "Ignotus, a megértő [Ignotus, the understanding]." (See Appendix C)

53. Ignotus. (2000). Búcsúztató [Eulogy]. In J. Meszaros (Ed.). *In memoriam Ferenczi Sándor* (pp. 37-42). Budapest, Hungary: Muhely. (Original work published 1933); Ignotus, as cited in Keve, "Ferenczi remembered," p. 5.

54. Jacques Lacan's notion of the *gaze*: The eye's look gives a sense of our self looking back at us of its own will. Lacan, J. (1978). The split between the

eye and the gaze. In *The four fundamental concepts of psychoanalysis* (J.-A. Miller, Ed.) (A. Sheridan, Trans.) (pp. 67-78). New York, NY: Norton. (Original work published 1973)

55. German tr., "the uncanny." Freud, S. (1919). Das Unheimliche [The uncanny]. *Imago, 5,* 297-324.

56. Khan, M. (1979). Secret as potential space. In S. A. Grolnick, L. Barkin, & W. Muensterberger (Eds.), *Between reality and fantasy: Transitional objects and phenomena* (pp. 259-270). New York, NY: Aronson.

57. Winnicott, D. W. (1965). The capacity to be alone. In *The maturational processes and the facilitating environment* (pp. 290-295). London, England: Hogarth Press and the Institute of Psycho-Analysis.

58. Ferenczi, S. (1949). Notes and fragments (1930-32). *International Journal of Psycho-Analysis, 30,* 231-242. Ferenczi's literary executors translated the bulk of these notes into German and published them in *The Bausteine, Vol. IV.* About a quarter of the notes are printed in this cited article.

59. Márai, S. (2002). *Embers* (C. B. Janeway, Trans). New York, NY: Vintage, 2002. (Original edition: *Candles burn down to the stump.* Budapest: Revai, 1942)

60. Kosztolányi, *Skylark,* p. 17.

61. Márai, *Embers,* p. 42.

62. Mayer, E. L. (2007). *Extraordinary knowing: Science, skepticism, and the inexplicable powers of the human mind.* New York, NY: Bantam,

63. Ibid, p. 139.

64. Freud compared thought transference to the sender and receiver as in telegraphing. Freud's papers touching on thought transference include "Dreams and Telepathy" (1922/1953); "Some Additional Notes on Dream Interpretation as a Whole" (1925/1961); "Dreams and Occultism" (1933/1965); and "Psychoanalysis and Telepathy" (1941/1973).

65. Rosso, D. (2015). "Das Unheimliche." Uncanny 2015 (Il perturbante) (Video file). Retrieved from https://www.youtube.com/watch?v=YEvLQqJ9KO8

66. Gyimesi, J. (2016). Why 'spiritism'? *International Journal of Psychoanalysis, 97*(2), p. 364.

67. Ibid, p. 379.

68. Ibid.

69. Freud & Ferenczi, *The correspondence*, Letter 406, p. 494.
70. Ibid., Letter 406, p. 495, footnote 5.
71. Ibid., Letter 74, pp. 79-81.
72. Ferenczi, S. (1963). Spiritism (N. Fodor, Trans.). *Psychoanalytic Review, 50(1)*, 143. (Original work published 1899).
73. Bromberg, P. M. (2011). *The shadow of the tsunami and the growth of the relational mind.* New York, NY: Routledge, pp. 137-138.
74. Mayer, *Extraordinary knowing*, pp. 214-215.
75. Ibid., p. 139.
76. Bromberg, *The shadow of the tsunami*, p. 141.
77. Ibid., p. 141.
78. Mayer, E. L. (2001). On "Telepathic dreams?" An unpublished paper by Robert Stoller. *Journal of the American Psychoanalytic Association, 49(2)*, 629-657, pp. 633-634.
79. Ibid., pp. 633-634. Highly relevant to the subjects I am discussing has been the work of Beebe, Fonagy, Lachmann, Sander, Stern, Trefarthen, Tronick, and others with regard to intersubjectivity, e.g. Sander's (2002) work on the "specificity of being known" and "rhythmicity," Lachmann and Beebe's (1996) paper on "heightened affective moments," Stern's (1985) work on affect attunement and "being together with another" (1995).

    In his chapter, "It Never Entered my Mind," Bromberg (2011) discusses the patient's dissociated self-states holding its own agenda about the patient's "secrets": "Through unfreezing the developmental process that Fonagy and his colleagues (2005) term *mentalization*, a patient becomes able, more freely and more safely, to experience another mind experiencing her mind experiencing their mind in those areas of mental functioning where dissociation had held intersubjectivity captive" (p. 45).
80. Freud & Ferenczi, *The correspondence*, Letter 132, p. 169.
81. Ibid., Letter 133, p. 171.
82. Ibid., Letter 141, p. 181.
83. Ibid., Letter 143, p. 183.
84. Ibid., Letter 21, p. 24.
85. Ibid., Letter 19, pp. 19-21. Author's license.
86. Ibid., Letter 166, pp. 212-213.

87. Ibid., Letter 183, p. 236. Author's license.

88. Schreber, D. P. (1955). *Memoirs of my nervous illness* (I. Macalpine & R. A. Hunter, Trans). New York, NY: New York Review of Books. (Original work published 1903)

89. Freud & Ferenczi, *The correspondence*. Letters 169, 171, 172, 173, & 183 describe Daniel Paul Schreber and the interest in the topic of paranoia.

90. Ibid., Letter 73, p. 76.

91. Ferenczi, S., & Groddeck, G. (2002). *The Sandor Ferenczi-Georg Groddeck correspondence, 1921-1933* (C. Fortune, Ed.) (J. Cohen, E. Petersdorff, & N. Ruebsaat, Trans.). New York, NY: Other Press, pp. 8-9.

92. Galvagno, R. (2011). Freud and Great Greece: Metamorphoses of the 'exotic' journey between ancient and modern imaginary. *Between*, *1*(2), 1-12, pp. 4-5.

93. Freud & Ferenczi, *The correspondence*, Letter 170, pp. 217-220. Author's license.

94. Ibid., Letter 127, p. 157.

95. Ibid., Letter 127, p. 157.

96. Georg Groddeck, considered the father of psychosomatic medicine; confidant of Freud, Ferenczi, and Jung.

97. Ferenczi & Groddeck, *Correspondence, 1921-1933*, pp. 8-9. Many authors, including me, have expressed similar thoughts as these.

98. Haynal & Haynal, "Ferenczi's attitude," pp. 52-73.

99. Kosztolányi, *Skylark*, p. 17.

100. Eakin, H. (2015, October 22). The terrible flight from the killing. *New York Review of Books*, §1, para. 20.

101. Bettelheim, B. (1982). *Freud and man's soul*. New York, NY: Knopf, pp. 8-9.

102. Ibid., p. 11.

103. Márai, S. (2013). *The withering world* (J. M. Ridland & P. V. Czipott, Trans.). London, England: Alma Books, p. 123.

104. Ibid., p. 141.

105. Kosztolányi, "Budapest, September 10, 1909." (See Appendix D)

106. Márai, *The withering world*, p. 141.

107. Ibid., p. 99.

108. E.g., Kosztolányi, "Budapest, September 10, 1909." (See Appendix D)

109. Márai. S. (2005). *Casanova in Bolzano* (G. Szirtes, Trans.) New York, NY: Vintage 2005, p. 16. (Original work published 1940)

110. Zweig, S. (2009). *Confusion* (A. Bell, Trans.). New York, NY: New York Review of Book, p. 85. (Original work published 1927)

111. Freud, S. (1957). On transience. In J. Strachey (Ed. & Trans.), The standard edition of the complete works of Sigmund Freud (Vol. 14, pp. 303-307). London, England: Hogarth Press, p. 306. (Original work published 1915)

112. Maso, C. (2000). *Break every rule: Essays on language, longing, and moments of desire.* Washington DC: Counterpoint, p. 23.

113. Felman, S. (1987). *Jacques Lacan and the adventure of insight.* Cambridge, MA: Harvard University Press, p. 11.

114. Carson, A. (1986). *Eros the bittersweet.* Princeton, NJ: Princeton University Press, p. 31.

115. Freud & Ferenczi, *The correspondence*, Letter 135, pp. 173-174.

116. Ibid. Ferenczi's Letter 135 describes the circle of sociologists, those interdisciplinary friends which were added and Ferenczi's enthusiasm for teaching. Footnotes 1-5 in this letter provide the historical content regarding Ferenczi's prospective students and the newspaper accounts of the oncoming Halley's Comet.

117. Lukács, *Budapest 1900.* Lukács provides rich details about the poet Endre Ady, describing how he was both political and a visionary for the Magyars. Lukács cites Zsigmond Móricz: "No one will ever be able to measure his impact on the entire youth of our time... Ady was the focus of passions that were burning in the minds of the masses; his poetry became the searchlight and the flamethrower,... and where his words fell the seed of power were cast in the souls of men" (pp. 164-165).

118. Ady, E. (n.d.). On the Hungarian fallow (B. Adams, Trans.), verse 1. Retrieved from http://www.visegradliterature.net/works/hu/Ady_Endre-1877/A_magyar_Ugaron/en/54500-On_the_Hungarian_Fallow/ (Original work published 1906)

119. Lukács, *Budapest 1900*, p. 165.

120. Karinthy, F. (1929). Lancszemek [Chain-links]. In *Minden maskeppen van* [Everything is otherwise] (pp. 85-90). Budapest, Hungary: Atheneum, pp. 1-3. Author's license.

121. Freud & Ferenczi, *The correspondence*, Letter 135, p. 174.

122. Ibid., Letter 127, p. 157.

123. Ibid., Letter 406, p. 495. Author's license.

124. Ibid., Letter 405, pp. 493-494. Author's license.

125. As cited in Moreau-Ricaud, "Healing boredom," p. 94.

126. Meszaros, *Ferenczi and beyond*, pp 20-30. Meszaros provides an excellent background to Ferenczi's work and the founding of the Budapest School.

127. Freud & Ferenczi, *The correspondence*, Letter 73, p. 75.

128. Ignotus, "Búcsúztató" [Eulogy]. In his eulogy for Ferenczi, Ignotus's final salute to Sándor's departing soul was to lock himself in his room and face a blank page.

129. Ignotus, as cited in Keve, *Ferenczi remembered*, pp. 2-6. Author's license.

130. Freud & Ferenczi, *The correspondence*, Letter 83, p. 96.

131. Ibid., Letter 73, pp. 75-77. Frau Seidler was a fascination for Ferenczi, who met with her to observe and experience her psychic abilities.

References

Ady, E. (n.d.). On the Hungarian fallow (B. Adams, Trans.), verse 1. Retrieved from http://www.visegradliterature.net/works/hu/Ady_Endre-1877/A_magyar_Ugaron/en/54500-On_the_Hungarian_Fallow/ (Original work published 1906)

Ady, E. (1906). *Uj versek* [New poems]. Budapest, Hungary: Pallas.

Babits, M. (1928). Az irástudók árulása [The treason of the literati], *Nyugat, 18*, pp. 1-17.

Babits, M. (1936). Kosztolányi, *Nyugat, 29*, pp. 395-401.

Balint, M. (1934). Dr. Sándor Ferenczi as psycho-analyst [Trans. of "Ferenczi Sándor, mint orvos"). *Indian Journal of Psychology, 20*, 312–315. (Original work published 1933)

Balint, M. (1949). Notes and fragments [1930-32]. *International Journal of Psycho-Analysis, 30*, 231–242.

Balint, M. (1958). Sándor Ferenczi's last years. *International Journal of Psycho-Analysis, 39*, 68.

Balint, M. (1968). *The basic fault.* New York, NY: Brunner/Mazel.

Balint, M. (1988). Notes for a preface by Michael Balint. In S. Ferenczi, *The clinical diary of Sándor Ferenczi* (J. Dupont, Ed.) (M. Balint & N. Z. Jackson, Trans.) (pp. 221–222). Cambridge, MA: Harvard University Press.

Balint, M. (2000). Ferenczi Sándor, mint orvos [Sándor Ferenczi as a physician]. In J. Meszaros (Ed.). *In memoriam Ferenczi Sándor* (pp. 148–154). Budapest, Hungary: Muhely. (Original work published 1933)

Baudelaire, C. (1857). *Les fleurs du mal* [The flowers of evil]. Paris, France: Poulet-Malassis.

Bettelheim, B. (1982). *Freud and man's soul.* New York, NY: Knopf.

Breton, A. (1990). *Communicating vessels.* Lincoln: University of Nebraska Press.

Bromberg, P. M. (2011). *The shadow of the tsunami and the growth of the relational mind.* New York, NY: Routledge.

Carson, A. (1986). *Eros the bittersweet.* Princeton, NJ: Princeton University Press.

de Waal, E. (2010). *The hare with amber eyes: A hidden inheritance.* New York, NY: Picador.

Devereux, G. (Ed.) (1953). *Psychoanalysis and the occult.* London, England: International Universities Press.

DuPont, J. (1988). Introduction. In S. Ferenczi, *The clinical diary of Sándor Ferenczi* (J. Dupont, Ed.) (M. Balint & N. Z. Jackson, Trans.) (pp. xi–xxvii). Cambridge, MA: Harvard University Press.

Eakin, H. (2015, October 22). The terrible flight from the killing. *New York Review of Books.* Retrieved from http://www.nybooks.com/articles/2015/10/22/terrible-flight-killing/

Esterházy, P. (2010). Introduction. In D. Kosztolányi, *Skylark* (R. Aczel, Trans.) (pp. vii–xv). New York, NY: New York Review of Books Classics.

Felman, S. (1987). *Jacques Lacan and the adventure of insight.* Cambridge, MA: Harvard University Press.

Ferenczi, S. (1924a). Ignotus, a megértő [Ignotus, the understanding]. *Nyugat, 23*. (English translation by A. Hagymasi, for C. R. Griffin, The Regular's Table Project; see Appendix C).

Ferenczi, S. (1924b). Altató és ébresztő tudomány (Levél Karinthy Frigyeshez) [Science that lulls and science that awakens (A letter to Frigyes Karinthy)]. *Nyugat, 17*, pp. 72-73.

Ferenczi, S. (1949a). Confusion of tongues between the adults and the child: The language of tenderness and of passion. *International Journal of Psycho-Analysis, 30*, 225-230.

Ferenczi, S. (1949b). Notes and fragments (1930-32). *International Journal of Psycho-Analysis, 30*, 231-242.

Ferenczi, S. (1955). The elasticity of psychoanalytic technique. In *Final contributions to the problems and methods of psychoanalysis* (M. Balint, Ed.) (E. Mosbacher, Trans.) (pp. 87-101). New York, NY: Basic Books. (Original work published 1928)

Ferenczi, S. (1963). Spiritism (N. Fodor, Trans.). *Psychoanalytic Review, 50*(1), 139-144. (Original work published 1899)

Ferenczi, S. (1980). Psychogenic anomalies of voice production. In S. Ferenczi, *Further contributions to the theory and technique of psychoanalysis* (J. Rickman, Ed.) (J. I. Suttie, Trans.) (pp. 105-109). New York, NY: Brunner/Mazel. (Original work published 1915)

Ferenczi, S. (1988). *The clinical diary of Sándor Ferenczi* (J. Dupont, Ed.) (M. Balint & N. Z. Jackson, Trans.). Cambridge, MA: Harvard University Press.

Ferenczi, S., & Groddeck, G. (2002). *The Sandor Ferenczi-Georg Groddeck correspondence, 1921-1933* (C. Fortune, Ed.) (J. Cohen, E. Petersdorff, & N. Ruebsaat, Trans.). New York, NY: Other Press.

Fiumara, G. C. (2013). *Psychoanalysis and creativity in everyday life.* New York, NY: Routledge.

Fonagy, P., Gergely, G., Jurist, E. L., & Target, M. (2005). *Affect regulation, mentalization, and the development of self.* New York, NY: Other Press.

Frank, T. (2009). *Double exile: Migrations of Jewish-Hungarian professionals through Germany to the United States, 1919–1945.* Bern, Switzerland: Lang.

Freud, S. (1919). Das Unheimliche [The uncanny]. *Imago, 5,* 297–324.

Freud, S. (1953). Dreams and telepathy. In J. Strachey (Ed. & Trans.), *The standard edition of the complete works of Sigmund Freud* (Vol. 8, pp. 195–220). London, England: Hogarth Press. (Original work published 1922)

Freud, S. (1957). On transience. In J. Strachey (Ed. & Trans.), *The standard edition of the complete works of Sigmund Freud* (Vol. 14, pp. 303–307). London, England: Hogarth Press. (Original work published 1916)

Freud, S. (1961). Some additional notes on dream interpretation as a whole. In J. Strachey (Ed. & Trans.), *The standard edition of the complete works of Sigmund Freud* (Vol. 19, pp. 127–138). London, England: Hogarth Press. (Original work published 1925)

Freud, S. (1965). Dreams and occultism. In J. Strachey (Ed. & Trans.), *New introductory lectures on psycho-analysis* (pp. 38–70) (Original work published 1933)

Freud, S. (1973). Psychoanalysis and telepathy. In G. Devereaux (Ed.), *Psychoanalysis and the occult* (pp. 56–68). New York, NY: International Universities Press. (Original work published 1941)

Freud, S., & Ferenczi, S. (1993). *The correspondence of Sigmund Freud and Sándor Ferenczi, volume 1, 1908–1914* (E. Brabant, E. Falzeder,

& P. Giampieri-Deutsch, Eds.) (P. T. Hoffer, Trans.). Cambridge, MA: Harvard University Press.

Galvagno, R. (2011). Freud and Great Greece: Metamorphoses of the 'exotic' journey between ancient and modern imaginary. *Between, 1*(2), 1-12. http://ojs.unica.it/index.php/between/article/view/312/295

Gay, P. (1988). *Freud: A life for our times.* New York, NY: Norton.

Gluck, M. (2016). *The invisible Jewish Budapest: Metropolitan culture at the fin de siècle.* Madison: University of Wisconsin Press.

Gluck, M. (2004). The Budapest flaneur: Urban modernism. *Jewish Social Studies, 10*(3), 1-22.

Gyimesi, J. (2016). Why 'spiritism'? *International Journal of Psychoanalysis, 97*(2), 357-383. https://doi.org/10.1111/1745-8315.12364

Hanák, P. (1998). *The garden and the workshop: Essays on the cultural history of Vienna and Budapest.* Princeton, NJ: Princeton University Press.

Harris, A., & Kuchuck, S. (Eds.). (2015). *The legacy of Sándor Ferenczi: From ghost to ancestor.* London, England: Routledge.

Haynal, A. (2016). The adventurous emigration of the Ferencziana: Contributions to their history. *Journal of the International Forum of Psychoanalysis.* https://doi.org/10.1080/080370 6X.2016.1200196

Haynal, A., & Haynal, V. (2015). Ferenczi's attitude (S. K. Wang, Trans.). In A. Harris & S. Kuchuck (Eds.), *The legacy of Sándor Ferenczi: From ghost to ancestor* (pp. 52-74). London, England: Routledge.

Ignotus. (1919). Halhatatlan Ady [Immortal Ady]. *Nyugat, 4-5,* pp. 223-224.

Ignotus. (2000). *Búcsúztató* [Eulogy]. In J. Meszáros (Ed.). *In memoriam Ferenczi Sándor* (pp. 37–42). Budapest, Hungary: Muhely. (Original work published 1933)

Karinthy, F. (1924). Altató és ébresztő tudomány (Válasz Ferenczi Sándornak) [The sleeping and waking science (Response to Sándor Ferenczi)]. *Nyugat, 17*, pp. 155–156.

Karinthy, F. (1929). Lancszemek [Chain-links] (Adam Makkai, Trans.). In *Minden maskeppen van* [Everything is otherwise]. Retrieved from https://djjr-courses.wdfiles.com/local--files/soc180:Karinthy-chain-links/Karinthy-Chain-Links_1929.pdf

Keve, T. (2012). Ferenczi remembered. In J. Szekacs-Weisz & T. Keve (Eds.), *Ferenczi and his world: Rekindling the spirit of the Budapest world* (pp. 1–29). London, England: Karnac.

Khan, M. (1979). Secret as potential space. In S. A. Grolnick, L. Barkin, & W. Muensterberger (Eds.), *Between reality and fantasy: Transitional objects and phenomena* (pp. 259–270). New York, NY: Aronson.

Kirk, J. (2013, October). Bartok's monster: Stalking the dead composer through Transylvania. *Harper's Magazine*, pp. 49–64.

Kosztolányi, D. (1924). *A bús férfi panaszai* [Laments of man of sorrow]. Budapest, Hungary: Franklin.

Kosztolányi, D. (1929). Budapest, 10 September, 1909. *Nyugat, 1*, pp. 21–34.

Kosztolányi, D. (1993). *Skylark* (R. Aczel, Trans.). New York, NY: New York Review of Books. (Original work published 1924)

Kosztolányi, D. (2011). *Kornél Esti* (B. Adams, Trans.) New York, NY: New Directions Books. (Original work published 1933)

Kristeva, J. (2004, December 2). *Thinking about liberty in dark times.* Holberg Prize acceptance speech at the Holberg Symposium, Bergen, Norway. Retrieved from https://www.holbergprisen.no/en/holberg-lecture-2004-thinking-about-liberty-dark-times

Krúdy, G. (1998). *The adventures of Sinbad* (G. Szirtes, Trans.). Budapest, Hungary: Central European University Press. (Original work published 1944)

Lacan, J. (1978). The split between the eye and the gaze. In *The four fundamental concepts of psychoanalysis* (J.-A. Miller, Ed.) (A. Sheridan, Trans.) (pp. 67-78). New York, NY: Norton. (Original work published 1973)

Lachmann, F., & Beebe, B. (1996). Three principles of salience in the patient-analyst interaction. *Psychoanalytic Psychology, 13*(1), 1-22. http://dx.doi.org/10.1037/h0079635

Lawrence, D. H. (2005) *Psychoanalysis and the unconscious and Fantasia of the unconscious.* Mineola, NY; Dover.

Loewald, H. (1972). The experience of time. *Psychoanalytic Study of the Child, 27*, 401-410. https://doi.org/10.1080/00797308.1972.11822722

Lorin, C. (1981). A propos de "L'amour de la science." *L'Evolution Psychiatrique, 46*(3), 755-771.

Lukács, J. (1988). *Budapest 1900: A historical portrait of a city and its culture.* New York, NY: Grove Press.

Makari, G. (2008). *Revolution in mind.* New York, NY: Harper.

Márai, S. (2000). The quick and the dead. In J. Meszáros (Ed.). *In memoriam Ferenczi Sándor* (pp. 47-50). Budapest, Hungary: Muhely. (Original work published 1933)

Márai, S. (2002). *Embers* (C. B. Janeway, Trans). New York, NY: Vintage, 2002. (Original work published 1942)

Márai. S. (2005). *Casanova in Bolzano* (G. Szirtes, Trans.) New York, NY: Vintage 2005. (Original work published 1940)

Márai, S. (2013). *The withering world* (J. M. Ridland & P. V. Czipott, Trans.). London, England: Alma Books.

Maso, C. (2000). *Break every rule: Essays on language, longing, and moments of desire.* Washington DC: Counterpoint.

Márai, S. (2013). *The withering world* (J. M. Ridland & P. V. Czipott, Trans.). London, England: Alma Books.

Mayer, E. L. (2001). On "Telepathic dreams?" An unpublished paper by Robert Stoller. *Journal of the American Psychoanalytic Association, 49*(2), 629–657.

McDonald, A. (2009). *Generation west: Hungarian modernism and the writers of the* Nyugat *review* (Doctoral thesis). University of British Columbia, Vancouver.

Meszáros, J. (Ed.). (2000). *In memoriam Ferenczi Sándor.* Budapest, Hungary: Muhely.

Meszáros, J. (2014). *Ferenczi and beyond: Exile of the Budapest School and solidarity in the psychoanalytic movement during the Nazi years* (T. A. Williams, Trans.). London, England: Karnac. (Original work published 2008)

Moreau-Ricaud, M. (1996). The founding of the Budapest school. In A. Bokay, P. Giampieri, & P. Rudnytsky (Eds.), *Ferenczi's turn in psychoanalysis* (pp. 41–59). New York, NY: New York University Press.

Moreau-Ricaud, M. (2012). Healing boredom: Ferenczi and his circle of literary friends. In J. Szekacs-Weisz & T. Keve (Eds.), *Ferenczi and his world: Rekindling the spirit of the Budapest world* (pp. 87–96). London, England: Karnac.

Ogden, T. H. (1997). Reverie and interpretation. *Psychoanalytic Quarterly, 66*(4), 567–595.

Phillips, A. (1994). Secrets. *London Review of Books, 16*(19), pp. 3–5.

Phillips, A. (2004). Desired desire. *London Review of Books, 26*(20/21), pp. 35-37.

Rosso, D. (2015). "Das Unheimliche." Uncanny 2015 (Il perturbante) (Video file). Retrieved from https://www.youtube.com/watch?v=YEvLQqJ9KO8

Rudnytsky, P., Bokay, A., & Giampieri-Deutsch, P. (Eds.). (1996). *Ferenczi's turn in psychoanalysis.* New York, NY: New York University Press.

Sander, L. W. (2002). Thinking differently: Principles of process in living systems and the specificity of being known. *Psychoanalytic Dialogues, 12*(1), 11-42. https://doi.org/10.1080/10481881209348652

Schreber, D. P. (1955). *Memoirs of my nervous illness* (I. Macalpine & R. A. Hunter, Trans). New York, NY: New York Review of Books. (Original work published 1903)

Staley, M. (2009). *The first Nyugat generation and the politics of modern literature: Budapest, 1900-1918* [Unpublished thesis]. Central European University, Budapest, Hungary.

Stern, D. N. (1985). *The interpersonal world of the infant.* New York, NY: Basic Books.

Stern, D. N. (1995). *The motherhood constellation.* New York, NY: Basic Books.

Stern, D. N., Sander. L. W., Nahum, J. P., Harrison, A. M., Lyons-Ruth, K., Morgan, A. C.,... Tronki, E. Z. (1998). Non-interpretive mechanisms in psychoanalytic therapy: The 'something more' than interpretation. *International Journal of Psycho-Analysis, 79* (Pt. 5), 903-921.

Szabo, M. (2015). *The door* (L. Rix, Trans.). New York, NY: New York Review of Books. (Original work published 1987)

Vida, J. (2005). Treating the "wise baby." *American Journal of Psychoanalysis, 65*(1), 3-12.

Winnicott, D. W. (1965). The capacity to be alone. In *The maturational processes and the facilitating environment* (pp. 290-295). London, England: Hogarth Press and the Institute of Psycho-Analysis.

Zweig, S. (2009). *Confusion* (A. Bell, Trans.). New York, NY: New York Review of Books. (Original work published 1927)

Acknowledgements

The Regulars' Table Project began in the middle of my analytic training when I realized I must be responsible for my *cure d'ennui*. My exposure to and interest in the work of Sándor Ferenczi and the Hungarian literati began with Judith E. Vida, who gently and generously introduced me to this thinking and shared her unique perspectives with grace over many years. These early experiences included Autobiographical Dialogue Seminars, followed by immersion in the community of The International Forum for Psychoanalytic Education (IFPE). Within this space, many deeply satisfying and enduring friendships began and continue.

With regard to these early days when The Regulars' Table stories were forming, I want to acknowledge the enthusiasm of Billy Brennan, who shared with me the allure and richness of early psychoanalytic history. Along this migration trail several other individuals gave their support, inspiration, and solidarity and shared their genuine excitement about the book.

My deepest thanks to André Haynal and Thomas Ogden for their part in this project's evolution.

Judit Meszáros was a welcoming presence in Budapest and shared her work and commitment to the International Sandor Ferenczi Society.

Andrea Hagymási provided the Hungarian-to-English translations of the original writing of several members of Ferenczi's regulars' table. I appreciate her literary background and enthusiasm for the upcoming Hungarian translation of this book.

This project could not have been undertaken without my deep friendships with Tom Archbald, who committed and prevailed, and Rachel Newcombe, trusted confidante and detective.

David James Fisher, Linda Carter, and Peter Hoffer gave insightful readings and genuine appreciation of the manuscript.

To Dr. Tibor Pal Seidler: I am amazed and grateful for your intuition about me, the vagabond, who might have passed on by. Implicitly, you recognized the old and new in each of us. Sensing each other without words, you defined the experience of the "finger of God."

Arnold Richards, Editor of IPBooks, was immediately decisive and found interest and value in this project.

My editor, Elizabeth McCarthy, engaged with an attention to detail and to the big picture. I received the gift of her literary and writing sensibilities. Her attunement to the readers of The Regulars' Table was most remarkable.

Jan Freya, copyeditor and beyond, I am grateful for your sophisticated technical abilities and sensing the aesthetic and intention of my mind in writing these stories, old and new.

I am so fortunate to have Lionel Corbett in my life. Who has generously supported, guided and best of all, understood my imaginative process.

I am blessed with a good family, Charles, Camilla, Raymond, and Rebecca, and have all the luck in the world to have such passionate and loyal daughters, Louise and Grace.

Christina Griffin, in *The Regulars' Table*, has created a genre of her own that moves smoothly, elegantly between quotations from Ferenczi's correspondence with Freud; Ferenczi's imagined thoughts; a literary love story told in the first person; an analytic discussion of "thought transference" and other inexplicable intersubjective phenomena; and finally a concatenation of the different voices that precede. Intellectual and literary history of early twentieth century Budapest, in Griffin's hands, read like poetry; and poetry and literature of the time helps bring the history of that era to life. *The Regulars' Table* is an imaginative piece of literature for which there is not a name; it is an experience not to be missed.

—Thomas H. Ogden, M.D., author most recently of *Reclaiming Unlived Life: Experiences in Psychoanalysis and The Hands of Gravity and Chance: A Novel*. Recipient of The Hans W. Loewald Memorial Award 2014, International Forum for Psychoanalytic Education.

Science or fiction, poetry or facts? It is all this. With Christina Griffin we embark on the atmosphere of a historic migration trail departing from a tiny geographical place in central Europe which leads us over the ocean. It is the journey of a conquest of the north-Atlantic world by the 20th century's Budapest culture—intertwined with psychoanalysis in an embrace, bringing innovative ideas and different sensibilities to the New Continent.

Among them: love, closeness, understanding and tolerance as a message. This volume lets you feel the atmosphere of a fairytale which could become reality.

—André E. Haynal, M.D., philosopher, physician, training and supervising analyst (IPA). Author of more than a dozen books including *The Technique at Issue: Controversies in Psychoanalysis; Disappearing and Reviving* and most recently *Encounters with the Irrational.* Leading scientific editor of the Freud/Ferenczi Correspondence (1992–2000) and recipient of the Sigourney Award for his life's work.

In this volume, psychoanalyst and historian Christina Griffin has given the reader an intimate series of glimpses into the life and times of Sándor Ferenczi, intimate friend and disciple of Sigmund Freud. Utilizing primary and secondary sources, fictionalized accounts of historical events and private musings about her own experiences and the workings of her mind, Dr. Griffin takes us on a wide-ranging journey in time and space that begins and ends in the coffee houses of fin-de-siècle Budapest, frequented by the group of writers, artists and intellectuals who helped shape Ferenczi's worldview. *The Regulars' Table* will capture the imagination of clinicians, academicians and anyone else with an interest in the cultural history of psychoanalysis.

—Peter Hoffer, Ph.D., Translator,
*The Correspondence of Sigmund Freud
and Sándor Ferenczi;*
Psychoanalytic Center of Philadelphia

CPSIA information can be obtained
at www.ICGtesting.com
Printed in the USA
LVHW021133030219
606198LV00006B/962/P